Key Stage 3
Classbook

Design
and
Technology

for September 2000

**Peter
Bull**

First published 2000
Reprinted 2000 (twice)

Letts Educational
9–15 Aldine Street
London W12 8AW
Tel 020 8740 2266
Fax 020 8743 8451

Text: © Peter Bull 2000

Design and illustrations © Letts Educational Limited 2000

Design and page layout: Ken Vail Graphic Design, Cambridge

Illustrations:Nick Hawken, Margaret Jones, Graeme Morris (Ken Vail Graphic Design), Sylvie Poggio Artists Agency (Phil Smith), SGA (Stephen Sweet, Mike Lacey)

Colour reproduction by PDQ Digital Media Solutions, Bungay, Suffolk

Picture research by Brooks Krikler Research

British Library Cataloguing-in-Publication Data

A CIP record for this book is available from the British Library

ISBN 1 84085 422 7

Printed and Bound in Spain

Letts Educational Limited, a division of Granada Learning Limited. Part of the Granada Media Group.

Acknowledgements

The author would like to thank the following for their assistance and guidance: Brian Williams, Brimsham Green School, Bristol; Michelle Dalley, Stratford High School; Wayne Samuel; Beryl Kelman.

The author and publishers are grateful to the following for permission to reproduce photographs:

Ariel Motor Company and Automotive Dynamics of Crewkerne: Unit 65.3; Cabaret Theatre, Covent Garden: 52.1, 54.1, 57.5; DATA Organisation/Parametric: 16.3; Dyson UK: 10.3; Economatics Ltd: 20.1, 65.1; Eye Ubiquitous: 10.1, 35.3, 61.3; Formech UK: 45.1; Frank Spooner Pictures: 10.4, 14.5, 17.4, 18.1, 35.2, 35.4, 36.4, 63.3, 84.3, 97.2, 98.2, 98.3, 100.4, 102.2, 102.4; James Davis Travel Photography: 52.3; John Walmsley Photography: 39.1, 101.2; NASA: 39.3, 59.3; Neil Lapham, Ashton Park School, Bristol: 19.1; Paul Nightingale: 17.1, 40.1, 85.3, 86.2, 87.1, 87.2, 87.3, 87.4, 93.1, 93.2, 93.3, 93.4; Peter Bull: 20.3, 21.2, 21.3, 21.4, 39.2, 45.4, 47.1, 47.2, 48.1, 48.3, 50.1, 50.2, 50.3, 50.4, 52.2, 52.4, 55.5, 58.4, 59.1, 59.2, 61.2, 64.2, 65.2, 67.4, 70.4, 74.2, 75.1, 76.1, 76.4, 79.1, 79.2, 80.1, 80.2, 86.1, 92.1, 92.4, 94.1, 94.2, 94.3, 96.1, 97.1, 97.3, 97.4; J.Polias (Australia), 10.2; The Royal Mint: 19.2; Solution Pictures: 64.3; Techsoft Ltd: 31.1, 31.2, 31.3, 31.4; Vantek Ltd: 76.3

Contents

Contents

Contents

Introduction

This Letts Design and Technology Classbook has been written to help you learn through your Key Stage Three course. It covers all the content of the National Curriculum and includes sections on Materials, Design, Food Technology and Textiles.

The book is divided into 103 units containing the important ideas you will need to know. Each unit begins with a list of the topics that you will cover. The information that follows is written clearly so that you can read the unit yourself. Answer the questions as you go along; these will help you focus on what you are reading. To answer some of the questions you may need to do extra reading by using the Internet or multimedia sources.

Each unit ends with a summary of the ideas that you should have become aware of as you worked through it. There is also a review activity, which has been written to help you to develop some topics further. These will also help with revision. Sometimes, you will be asked to research a topic and sometimes you will be asked to make something. You should be able to fit these activities to the project work you are doing in class.

Design and Technology is a very wide subject and each area needs different skills. However, you will find that you use certain skills across the subject. This book will help you to make the link between Materials, Graphics, Food and Textiles and will show you why each area is important. We hope that you will enjoy using this book and that you will continue to enjoy designing and making in the future.

1 Design Processes

In this section of the book you will learn the following things:

- how to use design processes;
- that design processes help to organise your thinking;
- that design processes are not fixed lists to be rigidly followed.

Designing

When you start **designing,** there are some questions that you need to ask. You cannot begin if you do not know what you are to design or its **context.** You need to know who it is for, what size it should be, its cost, how it is to be made, the materials or ingredients needed and any safety considerations (Fig 1). When you have started to design, you will have to make decisions and, probably, changes before you can start manufacture or **production**. You may still have to make changes, even while making, to produce a good final product. This constant improvement is an **iterative process**. Then you have to **evaluate** the product. Does it satisfy the needs of the customer or client? Is it safe to use? These questions must be asked for every design project whether it is a baby's toy, a dress, a meal or an aircraft.

▲ *Fig 1* *Thinking about choices.*

Q1 How could you find out exactly what a client wants you to make?

Processes

To try to simplify this thinking there are **design processes**. These have a number of steps: defining the problem, research, analysis, specification, developing proposals, planning, making and evaluation. There is no set order of steps and each one can be used any number of times for different design problems. If you have a container with coloured pencils in, then you pick the most suitable pencil. If you think of the design steps as pencils, when designing you pick up the most appropriate pencils as many times as you need to (Fig 2). Some designers start by making models and then evaluating them while others start by drawing lots of ideas and some look for existing things and develop from these (Fig 3). It's up to you to decide but do not leave out any steps!

▲ *Fig 2* Design steps.

Q2 What is the most likely starting point of any project?

Q3 What is the most likely finishing point of any project?

◄ *Fig 3* A successful project.

Key words

context – where the design need occurs

design processes – stages in putting your thoughts into a structure

designing – developing ideas and thinking about a project

evaluation – testing the product to see how well it suits the client

iterative process – process of constant assessment and improvement

production – making something

SUMMARY

■ Design processes help you to organise your thinking and consider all the parts of a design activity.

■ They are not fixed routines which you have to use each time.

■ They are iterative, you can jump backwards and forwards in the process to change, develop or modify your ideas at any time.

SUMMARY *activity*

Design a questionnaire which will remind you of the questions to ask when starting a design project. It should have spaces for you to write in your answers.

2 Design and make tasks

In this section of the book you will learn the following things:
■ why you need to do design and make tasks;
■ how focused tasks help you learn specific skills and knowledge;
■ the steps in design processes.

Open tasks

Design and make tasks or assignments (**DMT** or **DMA**) are sometimes called capability tasks and are **open** design projects, where you have to design, make and evaluate. They may take from a week to a whole term or more to complete. Your designing will be presented in a folio of sketches and drawings showing the development of your thinking, with an evaluation and technical notes added. You must remember that 'making' can mean making in resistant materials or textiles or food, or using the computer to make up lists, instruction sheets and charts. These tasks can start by identifying a need (Fig 1), or from a **design brief** from a client, by modelling ideas, by looking at existing **artefacts** or the work of designers past and present. When you start you may have little idea of what your end product will be. You must try to use all of the steps of a full design process.

Identification of need:
Old people often have difficulty gripping objects about the house from turning taps to opening bottles and tying laces. I am going to investigate what old people can do and have difficulty doing. I will then develop a design brief to focus on one area.

Design Brief
Design a device to help old people turn taps on and off. It must be easy to pick up from a flat surface.

Q1 Why do you need a design brief?

▲ *Fig 1*

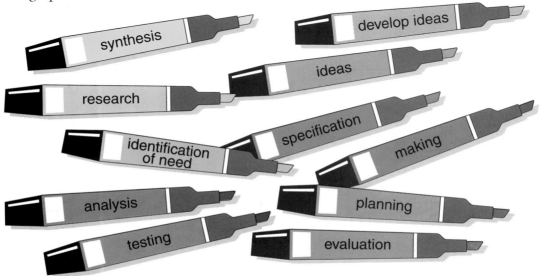

▲ **Fig 2** *The steps of a full design process.*

synthesis · develop ideas · ideas · research · identification of need · specification · making · analysis · planning · testing · evaluation

Focused tasks

Focused or resource tasks are used to help you learn particular skills or use a particular area of knowledge. They may take only a lesson or two. You cannot start to make a project unless you are able to measure and cut the material accurately. Your teacher may give you a small project to work on so that you can practise and improve your skills. This might be a design and make task which asks you to make something, perhaps with a small amount of designing or sketching.

The **outcome** may not be a complete, finished artefact but could be part of, or joined with, other focused tasks. For example, you could be asked to make a small brooch with a plastic base in order to learn to mark out and cut plastics. You could then learn how to emboss soft metal for the front decorative part. Joining the two together would complete the tasks (Fig 3).

Q2 What first skills would you need to work in textiles assuming you have learnt to measure and cut accurately?

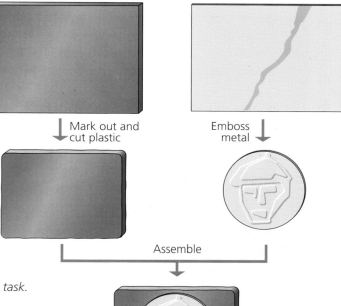

Mark out and cut plastic

Emboss metal

Assemble

► **Fig 3** Stages in a task.

Q3 Write down two ways you could join the parts of the brooch, i.e. join metal to plastic.

Key words

artefact – a manufactured object
design brief – a short statement about what is needed, who it is for, and any constraints
DMA – design and make assignment
DMT –design and make task
focused task – task which has a clearly defined result
open task – task which can have varied end results
outcome – the result of a design activity

SUMMARY

■ There are different types of tasks to help you develop your skills.
■ Short focused tasks help you learn and practise particular skills.
■ Long open tasks enable you to experience complete design processes and develop your ideas through to making.

SUMMARY *activity*

Make a list of six of the design properties of a kitchen utensil such as a kettle, toaster or mixer. What properties do you think the designer had in mind?

3 Sources of information

In this section of the book you will learn the following things:
- where to find information for your projects;
- who to ask for specialist information;
- how multimedia sources and the Internet can help you.

Research

When you start your topic or project, you may know very little about it and will have to do some research to find information that you can use. **Primary research** is information that you collect, for example when you ask people for their opinions. **Secondary research** is when you use information that others have written about or collected. It is important to write down the **source** including the author's name, the title, the date and where you found it. A list of the sources you have used should appear in your folio or notes. This list is your **bibliography**.

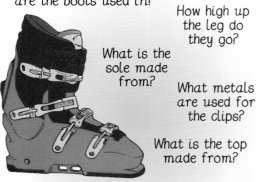

What temperature range are the boots used in?

How high up the leg do they go?

What is the sole made from?

What metals are used for the clips?

What is the top made from?

What is the sole made from?

How do they fit the skis?

How light are they?

▲ **Fig 1** *Researching ski boots.*

You can write to companies to ask about their products; they nearly always answer and often send you information. Tell them what you are doing, but keep your letter short, to the point and polite!

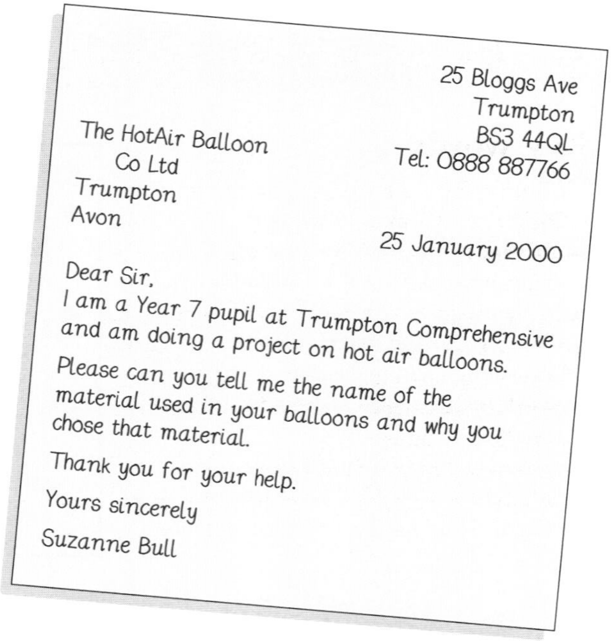

Q1 Why is it necessary to do research and not use only your ideas?

If you are contacting people to ask them questions or for advice, do it in plenty of time as it may take businesses over two weeks to answer. Think about using e-mail; it is much quicker.

It is important to seek help from people with a real knowledge of the subject. For example, if you are researching sports clothes, then ask a range of people who play sport for their opinions and ideas. The more you ask, the more balanced a view you may get (Fig 1).

▶ **Fig 2** *A letter asking for information.*

25 Bloggs Ave
Trumpton
BS3 44QL
Tel: 0888 887766

The HotAir Balloon
Co Ltd
Trumpton
Avon

25 January 2000

Dear Sir,

I am a Year 7 pupil at Trumpton Comprehensive and am doing a project on hot air balloons.

Please can you tell me the name of the material used in your balloons and why you chose that material.

Thank you for your help.

Yours sincerely

Suzanne Bull

Local businesses are usually helpful if you visit. Try to choose times when they are not too busy – it may be sensible to phone first. Make a **questionnaire** to remind you to ask the same questions each time and write down the answers. To save time you could leave it with them to complete.

> **Q2** Give three things that you have to think about when you are designing a questionnaire.

There are many **specialist** books and magazines which you could read or contact and there may be newspaper articles which could be of use. For major projects, it is a good idea to build up a scrapbook.

Multimedia

There are lots of **multimedia** sources such as encyclopedias, specialist catalogues and manufacturer's data on **CD-ROM** which can be cut and pasted easily into your work (Fig 3). Do not forget the Internet with its millions of pages on almost everything. You must take care to check information from the Internet with other reputable sources, as you have no guarantee that it is true or correct.

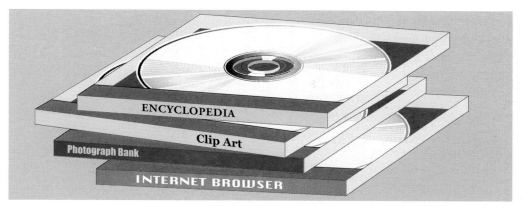

ENCYCLOPEDIA

Clip Art

Photograph Bank

INTERNET BROWSER

▲ *Fig 3*

Q3 What advantages are there in using multimedia sources for your work?

Key words

bibliography – a list of sources of information
CD-ROM – Compact disc read only memory
multimedia – sound, text and pictures in electronic form
primary research – research which you collect
questionnaire – a list of questions with spaces for written answers
secondary research – research collected and published by others
source – where you find information
specialist – relating to and expert in specific areas

SUMMARY

- There are lots of sources of information available: from individuals, companies, books and the Internet.
- You must write down the sources of all the information you use.
- It is important to list the ones you use in your folio or notebook.

SUMMARY activity

Write a letter to the Adidas company telling them that you are doing a project on sports shoes. Ask three questions about the design of their training shoes for young people.

4 Mapping your ideas

In this section of the book you will learn the following things:
- why using brainstorming and bubble diagrams is a good idea;
- how to use brainstorming to help your thinking;
- how to use concept maps to help your revision.

Brainstorming

Some of the best inventions have come from people who have tried something which others have not even thought about. Making this move to original thinking is difficult. Using **brainstorming** and **bubble diagrams** is a way of putting your thoughts down on paper quickly – the good ones and the apparently foolish ones. Writing them down quickly often shows up new links that you would not normally think of. First, draw a bubble in the centre of your page and write in your starting word, then draw new bubbles coming from the centre one. These can contain any connected words. Each bubble can have any number of **links**, and you can add them as you think of them (Fig 1). When you have completed your diagram, you may need to take one of the bubbles and develop it further. This can be done on a new sheet of paper. Include all of your thoughts, as even the ones that may appear trivial and unimportant may eventually lead you to exciting new design ideas.

Q1 Why is drawing a bubble diagram sometimes better than writing a list of ideas?

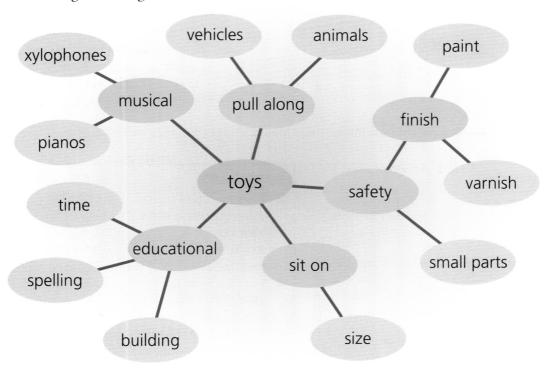

▲ **Fig 1** *Typical bubble diagram for a project.*

It is often these 'foolish' words which can lead you towards novel ideas. A bubble diagram can be used to decide what you are going to do at the start of designing. However, you can always take one of the bubbles from any diagram and use that as a new starting point or to work on a small part of a project. To show the decisions you choose, you can colour the relevant linking lines (Fig 2).

Q2 How could you show on a bubble diagram which decisions were important to you and which you actually chose?

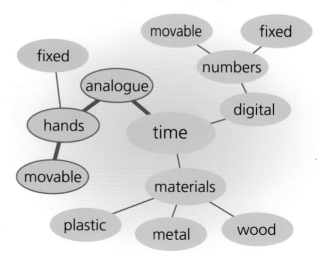

▲ **Fig 2** A bubble diagram showing coloured links.

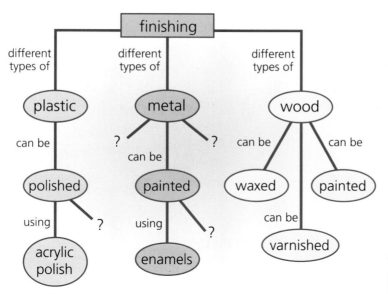

▲ **Fig 3** A concept map about finishes.

Mapping

Concept mapping looks similar to bubble diagrams; each bubble contains a word and on the line connecting two bubbles is a statement which also connects them (Fig 3). You can therefore check on what you know and what you do not know. Concept mapping is a useful revision aid by using key words to link to other words.

Q3 Why would you use a concept map and not a bubble diagram?

Key words

brainstorming – a technique for writing down linked ideas quickly

bubble diagram – a diagram of your ideas

concept map – a map of understanding and learning

links – connections between bubbles

SUMMARY

- Brainstorming is a good quick way to write down your ideas about a topic.
- It makes it easy to link or identify new ideas, so you can investigate areas that you might not have thought of originally.
- Concept maps enable you to draw a diagram of relationships between key words of a topic.
- They are useful for your revision.

SUMMARY activity

Draw a bubble chart based on an educational toy for a three-year-old child, e.g. learning to tell the time.

5 Proposals

In this section of the book you will learn the following things:
- why design proposals are needed;
- how design proposals are matched to the specifications;
- what should be included in your design proposals.

Proposals

Proposals are your decisions about how you are going to do your designing and making. They make up your outline planning. The specification has a list of design **criteria**. These are the points which your project must have. You must make sure that your proposals match these criteria, and also consider appearance, **function** and safety (Fig 1).

Appearance
It must be attractive to look at, appeal to a young child.
It must have a good feel.

Function
It should be a toy to interest a six-year-old.
It must have moving parts, and make some noise when operated.

Safety
The finish must be safe.
There should be no small parts.
Every part should be fixed securely.
No sharp edges.

▲ **Fig 1** Matching the criteria.

6 October 2000
Decided to round off the edges of the back of the toy to make it nicer to handle.

16 October 2000
Thinking about finishes, wood dyes instead of paint ... not toxic ... easier to apply. Will show grain.

20 October 2000
Make top from acrylic sheet instead of wood, self-coloured and shiny already ... less work.

▲ **Fig 2** The diary.

Q1 Why is it important to write down any changes you make in your proposals?

Planning

Everyone finds it difficult to plan accurately – some things may take longer than you think. For example, you may not be able to get the materials just when they are needed. Sometimes, when you start you will find it impossible to make parts in the way you intended. You will have to change or modify your proposals to ensure that the product matches your specification. Always write down why you have made the changes you make. You could record the changes by using a diary (Fig 2).

Telling others obout your project

From time to time, you may have to tell your teachers and classmates about your proposals. Sometimes making simple models will help them understand what you are trying to do. **Modelling** is a useful way for you to explore and develop your proposals.

All designers set themselves **timetables** for their work. Your teacher will tell you how long you have for each topic or project. You should allow time for thinking, researching, drawing, modelling, making and evaluation.

If you use word processing or computer-aided design (**CAD**) packages to draw up your proposal and planning sheets, they can be easily developed and modified; try to use graphical methods to make your plans clear. A Gantt chart will help you plan your activities, especially those with start and finish times that overlap (Fig 3).

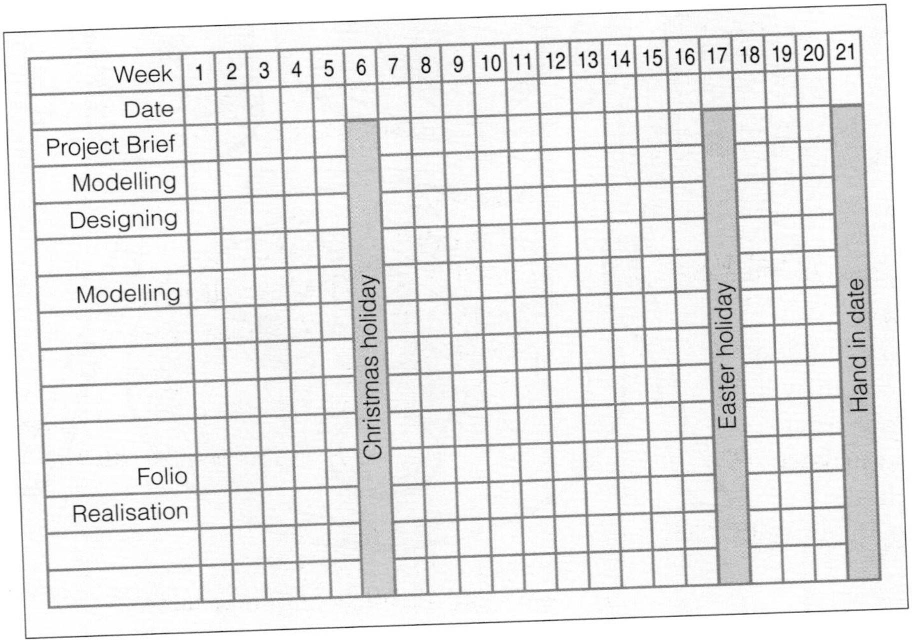

◀ *Fig 3* A Gantt chart.

Q2 Are thinking, researching, drawing, modelling, making and evaluation all likely to take equal amounts of time?

Q3 What things are likely to make you need to change your plans or proposals?

Key words

CAD – computer-aided design
criteria – requirements which must be met
function – what a product does
modelling – making small-scale replicas or using a computer program to test ideas or topics.
proposals – the things you intend to do
timetable – a chart showing when you hope to complete parts of the project

SUMMARY

■ Design proposals tell others how you are going to complete your project, what will happen when, and how you are sure that the specification will be met.

■ Properly devised design proposals will match the specification and enable you to check that your product will be satisfactory.

SUMMARY *activity*

Draw a planning chart with vertical spaces (columns) for the stages of the project, and horizontal spaces (rows) for the dates or weeks. You could keep this and photocopy it for future use.

6 Specifications

In this section of the book you will learn the following things:

■ what a product design specification is;
■ how to write a specification;
■ how to evaluate your product against the specification.

Starting the product design

The product design **specification** tells others, such as the user or client, what you as the designer are going to make. Your design **brief** will be a short statement saying what you are attempting to design and make. When you have written or been given the brief, you need to think about your specification. This will be a list of all the things that the **product** must have or do. Will the product look right? Will it do the job it was intended to do? How big does it need to be? What colour will it be? For example, your brief may say 'Design and make a meal for a young child's birthday party' (Fig 1).

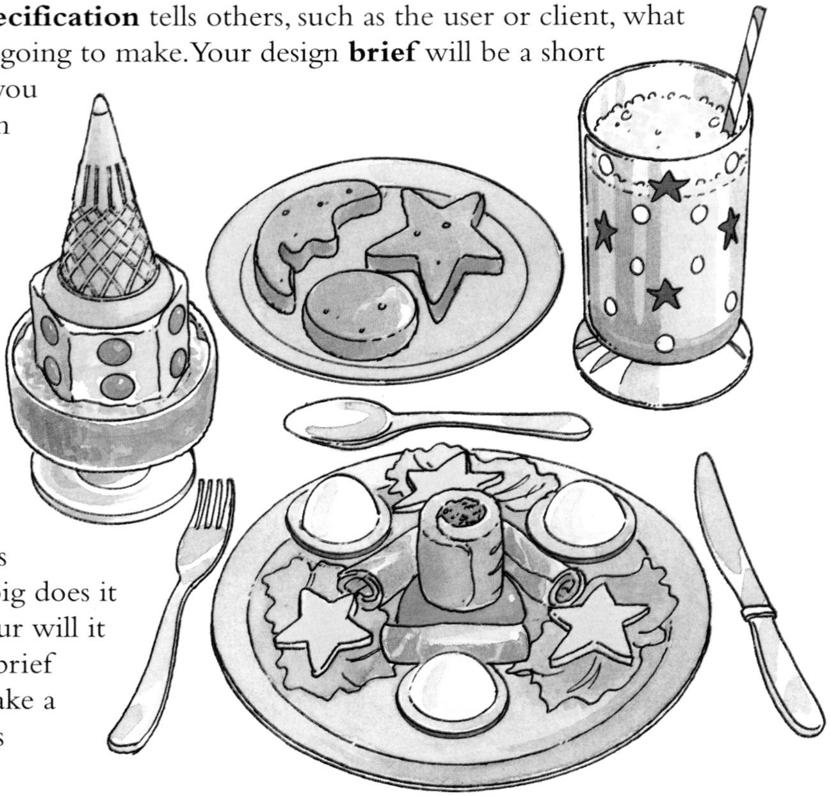

▲ **Fig 1** *A meal for a children's party.*

A specification

The specification might be written in this form.

The meal must be:

■ attractive to children from 6 to 8 years old
■ easily prepared the day before
■ cost no more than £3 for each child
■ contain both savoury and sweet courses
■ based on the theme of 'Space Food'
■ free of junk food
■ able to fit on a tray sized 400 mm by 400 mm.

Q1 What could be two requirements of a 'fun radio for children's use'?

▲ **Fig 2** *A child's fun radio.*

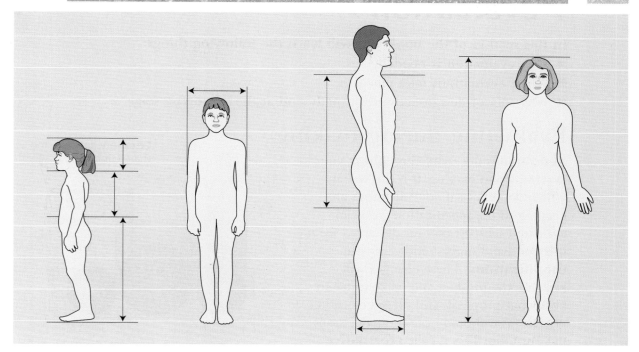

▲ **Fig 3** Anthropometric data.

Checking the specification

When you have finished the making, you need to look at the specification and your product and compare the two. If you keep referring to your specification during designing, you are less likely to end up with something that does not match the specification. It is not generally a good idea to change the specification once the project is started.

Q2 Why is it not a good idea to change the specification once you have started the project?

Q3 What is the difference between a design brief and a specification?

When moving from the brief to the specification, you must talk to the prospective user to find out their needs. If this is not possible, for instance if the user is a very young child, then you must look at information written about young children such as **ergonomic** or **anthropometric data** (Fig 3).

Key words

anthropometric data – data about the sizes and measurement of people, what they can reach and hold, etc.
brief – a short statement about what you intend to do
ergonomic data – data about how people relate to the things they use
product – the finished article
specification – what the product has to do and look like; a list of design requirements

SUMMARY

- Writing out a specification can help you check that the product is what the client intended.
- The specification explains who the product is for, its purpose, ingredients, materials, sizes, colour, etc.
- You must be sure that it is done carefully and is correct.

SUMMARY activity

Select a gadget that you use regularly and write a designer's specification for it. What do you think the designer thought about when starting to write his or her own specification?

7 Evaluation

In this section of the book you will learn the following things:
- why evaluation is needed;
- when evaluations take place;
- why school design activities usually end at the prototype stage.

Evaluating during making

Evaluation is necessary throughout your designing and making. It is the way in which you check if your decisions are keeping to the specification. You can evaluate each part of your design to see if it is good and suggest and carry out **modifications**. These changes will improve the product and make it match both your proposals and the specification criteria. You should note these decisions in your folio. This is called **formative evaluation** (Fig 1).

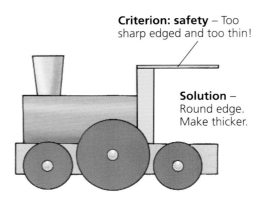

Criterion: safety – Too sharp edged and too thin!

Solution – Round edge. Make thicker.

▲ *Fig 1* *Toy safety.*

Q1 Why is it essential to do formative evaluation during your project?

Evaluating when finished

Summative evaluation happens at the end of the project when you check the final product against the specification. The real test is to let the client or other people use and comment on it. What do they think of the product? Does it satisfy the need? It is not good enough just to say, 'I like it, so its OK !' You must give good reasons why you like it, based on fact. You should also say where your product does not meet the specification and why. It is a good idea to ask someone who has had nothing to do with the project as they may comment on things that you or your teacher have not considered (Fig 2).

▲ *Fig 2* *Talking about your project.*

Finally, you should say how the product could be improved and what you would do next. Remember that, in school, the product is usually a **prototype** because of limited time. If this design problem was in industry, the product would be evaluated and modified over and over again until a really acceptable one was achieved. It would be tested by the intended users to say what they felt about the product; changes would then be made before full **production**.

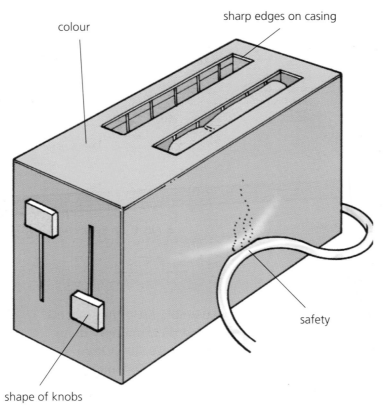

colour

sharp edges on casing

safety

shape of knobs

▲ **Fig 3** *What's wrong with the design?*

Existing products

You can also evaluate existing products. For example saying what you like or dislike about a computer game or electric toaster will often help you in your own design thinking. Suggesting how the design could be improved will give you some ideas about the designer's thinking (Fig 3).

Q2 If your product was a curry, write down three points on which you could evaluate it.

Q3 Why is it necessary for producers to evaluate and modify products many times before full production?

Key words

formative evaluation – an on-going evaluation
modification – changing something
production – making the product
prototype – a first working model or product
summative evaluation – the final evaluation

SUMMARY

■ Formative evaluation helps you to continually improve and modify your ideas during designing and making, by referring to your specification and checking how close you are to it.

■ Summative evaluation happens at the end of the making. It checks if your product suits the purpose for which it was intended and should show how you could improve it.

SUMMARY activity

Design a chart to evaluate bicycles. Include at least ten different points on which you would evaluate them, e.g. safety and ease of use. (You can use these two!)

8 Costing

In this section of the book you will learn the following things:
- the importance of accurate costing;
- using computer programs to make component, ingredient and cutting lists;
- understanding the human and environmental costs.

How much?

It is important to know how much your project will cost to make. You may have to pay for it or cost may be one of your specification's criteria. The best way to make a list of your **components** is to use a **spreadsheet program** such as *Excel*. This will allow you to add up columns and rows, work out changes or multiply the whole list.

	A	B	C	D	E
1	Number	Ingredient	Weight in grams	Pence per kilo	Total cost
2					
3		butter	110	200	22.0
4		caster sugar	50	120	6.0
5		plain flour	110	150	16.5
6		rice flour	50	200	10.0
7					
8					
9				total	54.5

▲ **Fig 1** An Excel *chart*.

For example, you can make up a list of ingredients with prices for one meal and then multiply them for a meal for ten people automatically. Often the price quoted by the supplier for wood, metal or plastics is for a large sheet or panel (Fig 2). By using simple formulae in a spreadsheet, you can easily work out the cost of the sizes that you need. You can save your spreadsheet, change it and print it out at any time.

▲ **Fig 2** How much material?

Q1 You could draw up a list with pen and paper. What are the advantages of using a computer for costing?

By using lists of priced ingredients, you can modify your ingredients to be more economical and try out the effect of changes. Cutting lists can be used to adjust sizes to make the best use of **stock sizes** and so save you the time of cutting materials to size and wasting materials.

Q2 How can using lists of priced materials help to save you money?

Knowing the cost of each material or ingredient allows you to make choices based on price. If your project is too expensive, then you can easily change some materials or ingredients for cheaper ones.

In school, we only consider the material costs, but there are manufacturing costs such as electricity, gas and replacement of equipment and tools.

gold? platinum? silver? steel?

▲ **Fig 3** How much will it cost?

Using materials wisely

All materials come at a human and environmental cost so they should come from renewable resources and be **recycled**. They should not pollute the environment either during manufacture, use or when finished with. Sometimes in this country we use cheap materials from the Third World where production may have less regard for worker safety or the environment.

Q3 How would you find out the cost of materials?

Key words

components – parts of a project

recycling – reusing waste or unwanted materials

spreadsheet program – a computer program such as *Excel* which stores data and allows it to be manipulated

stock sizes – the standard sizes which suppliers have in stock

SUMMARY

■ Accurate pricing of materials will help you use materials more economically.

■ Using a spreadsheet will allow you to test out, change and estimate how much material you need.

■ In any project, there are hidden costs of manufacturing such as energy requirements and wear and tear of tools and machinery.

SUMMARY *activity*

Make up your own headings for a components price list, similar to the one below, which can be photocopied to be used in your projects. Increase the number of rows as necessary.

Material	Height	Width	Length	Price	Number required	Total cost

9 Design decisions

In this section of the book you will learn the following things:
■ how to prioritise your decisions;
■ the implications of the decisions you take;
■ how to cope with mistakes.

While you are designing there will be many decisions to be taken. Some will be easy, others will have effects which you may not be able to predict. Good planning will help you reduce these to the minimum.

Q1 What sorts of decisions might you have to take when designing?

Priorities

You must **prioritise** to make sure that those parts of your project which require special treatment are tackled at the right time. You may have to order materials which could take time to arrive, so order them at the beginning and then continue with something else until they arrive. You may have to wait to use certain equipment until it is not in use by others.

6 October 2000
Check with teacher if textiles in stock.
If not where can I get them?
How long will it take?
What can I do until they arrive?

12 October 2000
Make sure computer knitting machine is working.
See technician.
Ask her to book it for Tuesday next week.

20 October 2000
Patterns should be ready by today.

▲ *Fig 1* A list of priorities.

Implications

At other times you may not know the effects or **implications** of any changes you intend to make. You must think through any decisions you take, especially if they happen late in your designing. You may find that the method you were going to use is no longer possible because of materials or tools not being available. You will then have to find alternative materials, tools or processes to replace the ones you cannot use.

Making a net for a box for your project

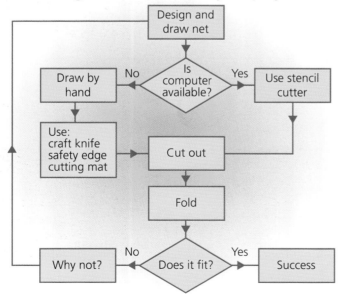

▲ *Fig 2* Options flow chart.

Reconciliation

At some stage, you will have to change some aspect of your project and this may cause more problems. Try to anticipate problem areas in advance.

Irreversible decisions

Some decisions may be **irreversible** – once taken you cannot go back. You may cut your textiles too small or add an ingredient at the wrong time to a recipe. You must quickly make up your mind what you are to do. Can you recover from this mistake? How are you going to progress? Will it ruin the project completely? You should write down your options and then make a decision. It is no good wasting time and getting frustrated about the mistake.

Q2 What are the implications of not having the right equipment for your project?

Q3 If you measure and cut something incorrectly, what can you do about it?

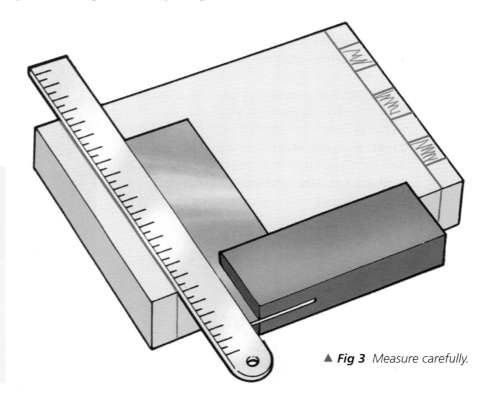

▲ **Fig 3** Measure carefully.

Key words

implication – what is going to happen as a result of a decision taken
irreversible – once something has been done, it cannot be changed
priority – the order in which things need to be done
reconciliation – deciding to do things in a way that may not be your first choice

SUMMARY

- Decisions have to be taken during designing and making.
- You must decide the order in which parts of your project are done.
- All decisions have some effects later on.
- You will not be able to change the results of some decisions.

SUMMARY activity

Use one of your recent projects and make a flow chart of the decisions that you took.

10 Designers, past and present

In this section of the book you will learn the following things:
- why it is important to look at past and present designers and makers;
- where to find information about designers and makers;
- how the Internet helps you with your research.

Experience

When you are **designing**, your ideas might come from things you have seen, read or heard about or from your own experience. This might influence the way you think. You might like or dislike certain foods, clothes or games and this will influence how you design. If you rely just on your own experience, then you may not explore a wide range of ideas. In order to widen your own experience, you should look at the work of designers and makers. You should ask questions such as, 'What was the designer thinking about when he or she designed this?' or 'Are these designs, original or are they developed from existing ones?'

> **Q1** Give one question to ask, which would help you understand a designer's work.

There are many sources of information about designers: the large museums such as the Victoria and Albert Museum in London, libraries, books, the Internet and CD-ROMs.

> **Q2** What advantages are there in visiting a museum to see the designer's work instead of reading about it?

▲ **Fig 1** *A Charles Rennie Mackintosh table in Glasgow School of Art, also designed by Mackintosh.*

Multimedia sources

Using the Internet or CD-ROMs is a great way to see the work of many designers, because you can download text and pictures. You can search for **multimedia** information about different periods, such as Art Deco special materials like textiles or glass, or certain areas of fashion or architecture.

▼ **Fig 2** *Internet page about a designer.*

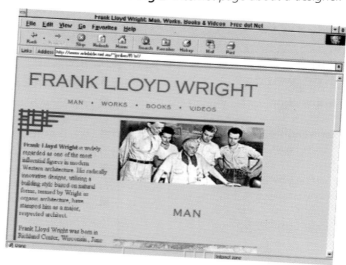

Most encyclopedias will usually include the famous designers. These are a few of them:

Isambard Kingdom Brunel – bridges, tunnels
Charles Rennie Mackintosh – furniture, houses, painting (Fig 1)
Norman Foster – architecture
Terence Conran – home furnishing
Vivien Westwood – fashion/textiles
James Dyson – vacuum cleaners (Fig 3)
Dr Alex Moulton – small-wheeled bicycles
Sir Alex Issigonis – Mini car (Fig 4)
Ferdinand Porsche –Volkswagen Beetle
H.C. Beck – The Underground map
René Lalique – jewellery and glass

▶ **Fig 3** *A Dyson vacuum cleaner.*

Q3 What advantages are there in using CD-ROMs or the Internet to find information about designers?

▲ **Fig 4** *BMC Minis.*

Key words

designing – thinking of and developing ideas
multimedia – sound, pictures, text, video in digital form

SUMMARY

■ You can improve your own designing by looking at other designer's work.
■ Try to read and look at as many sources as possible and ask yourself questions about the work you see.
■ The Internet is a great place to find multimedia information – there are many different sites about the same designer, giving you access to different opinions about the work.

SUMMARY ☞
activity
Take one designer from the list above and make an A4 poster about him or her.

11 Sketching

In this section of the book you will learn the following things:
- how to model your ideas using sketching;
- making your design drawings easy to understand;
- using crating to draw complicated shapes.

It is much easier to describe something by drawing than by writing about it. When you are designing and modelling ideas by drawing, you must be able to get ideas onto paper quickly. They sometimes come quickly and if you take a long time drawing, you will forget the ideas before you can draw them. This is why using a computer at this stage is probably not a good idea.

Ideas onto paper

Sometimes we talk about 'rough' drawings. We mean 'quick' drawings, as no one wants to see poor or scruffy work nor do we want to see drawings which have been neatened up after the designing. They lose their spontaneity. You need to **sketch** your ideas simply and quickly, with cut-aways, **exploded diagrams** and different views to show any complicated parts which may be difficult to develop or understand. You are drawing for two reasons: to develop your ideas into a workable project and for others to see how you are progressing.

Q1 Why should sketching be done quickly?

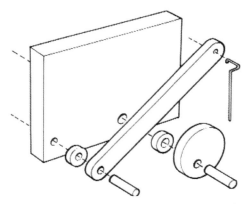

▲ **Fig 1** An exploded diagram.

Include all your ideas

You must try to put down all your ideas because, although you may discount some at the beginning, you might come back to develop them into a project. Lay out your drawings in a logical manner on the paper so that others can follow them. When sketching, you should use an HB pencil – too soft a pencil is easily smudged. This will still allow you to put some shading into your sketches. To protect your drawing, use paper under your hand to prevent smudging. If you use **crating**, you will find it easier to draw complex shapes at various angles. Draw the crates as lightly as possible and do not rub them out (Fig 3).

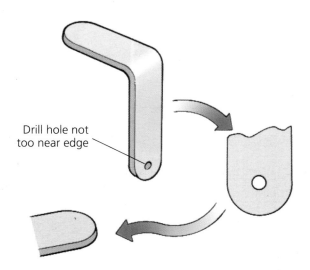

Drill hole not too near edge

▲ **Fig 2** Using arrows to show the way.

Practise drawing crates so that you can do it quickly and easily. By distorting the crates, i.e. making them narrower at the back than the front, a simple **perspective** effect can be achieved (Fig 4). When drawing is complete, you can then go over the outside edges to create a three-dimensional effect (Fig 5).

Q2 Why should you use an HB pencil for sketching?

Q3 How does crating help you draw complex shapes?

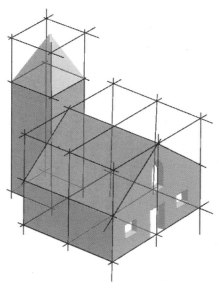

▲ **Fig 3** Crating.

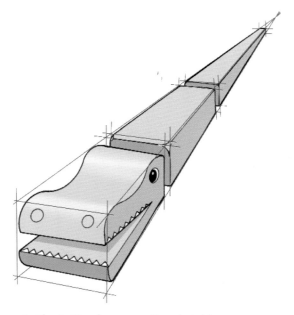

▲ **Fig 4** Simple perspective sketching.

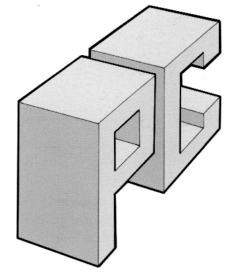

▲ **Fig 5** Thick and thin lines.

Key words

crating – using lightly drawn boxes for guidance
exploded diagrams – showing how all the parts fit together
perspective – giving an impression of depth
sketching – using a pencil freehand

SUMMARY

- Sketching helps you to develop your ideas.
- It needs to be quickly done so that you do not forget your ideas.
- Crating helps you draw more complicated shapes.
- Varying the weight of the line can create a three-dimensional effect.

SUMMARY *activity*

Use crating to draw a piece of furniture in your home.

12 Isometric projection

In this section of the book you will learn the following things:
- why isometric projection is used;
- using isometric grids;
- how to make exploded diagrams.

Using a grid

Sketching and crating is done **freehand**, i.e. without the use of rules or straight edges. The purpose is to get your ideas down onto paper as quickly as possible. Crating is an aid to getting a more realistic look to your drawing. Isometric projection is a way of drawing using a grid of lines which are at 30° to the horizontal (Fig 1). This will enable you to draw good pictorial sketches of parts of your work. The grid is sometimes used under the sheet of paper on which you are drawing. On pages 214 and 215 there are grids that can be photocopied for this purpose.

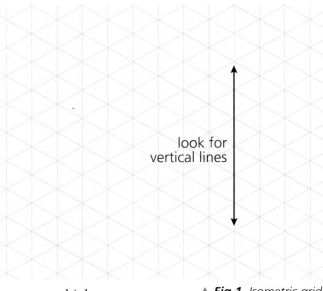

look for vertical lines

▲ **Fig 1** *Isometric grid.*

Q1 Why is crating used?

Lines at right angles

When you start to draw an object, first draw the front edge – this will be a vertical line (Fig 2). Then you will be able to draw the four lines towards the back of the object, i.e. two from the top and bottom of the vertical line. If you are unsure how long the lines will be, you can count the blocks. If the object that you are drawing has right angles, then all the drawn lines will follow the lines on the **isometric grid**.

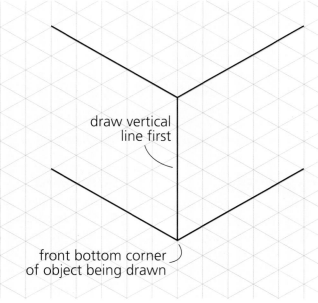

draw vertical line first

front bottom corner of object being drawn

▲ **Fig 2** *Starting an isometric projection.*

Lines at other angles

Lines which are not at right angles will not follow the grid and will have to be estimated. If you practise drawing boxes, and arranging them slightly away from each other, you will be able to make exploded diagrams. Where boxes overlap in your drawing, you will need to draw them in lightly at first. When you have completed this stage, you can draw in the lines which are showing (Fig 5).

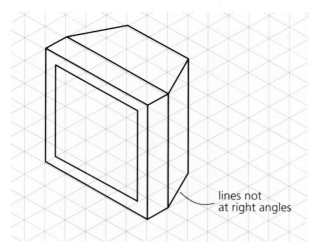

▲ **Fig 3** Lines which are not at right angles.

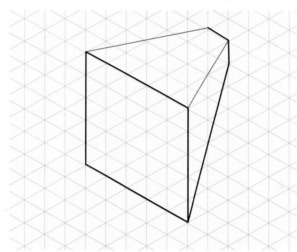

▲ **Fig 4** Using light lines.

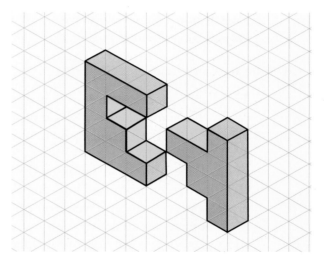

▲ **Fig 5** Exploded diagram.

lines not at right angles

Q2 At what angles are the lines on an isometric grid?

Q3 What does an exploded view show?

Q4 Why in an exploded diagram should you draw in the lines lightly at first?

Key words

freehand – drawing without using rules or straight edges

isometric grid – grid with vertical lines and at 30° to horizontal

SUMMARY

- Isometric projection is an aid to drawing three-dimensional objects.
- It uses isometric grids which have lines at 30 degrees to the horizontal.
- Grids with thick enough lines to show through drawing paper can be used as an aid to sketching.

SUMMARY activity

Use an isometric grid to draw an exploded diagram of a simple object e.g. a toy.

13 Orthographic projection

In this section of the book you will learn the following things:
- what orthographic projections are;
- the views shown in orthographic projections;
- using computer-aided design packages.

Working drawings

Orthographic drawings are working drawings which contain all the information necessary to make a product. They contain all the measurements, construction details and how the parts fit together. If the project is complicated with lots of parts, it may take several drawings to give all the information (Fig 1).

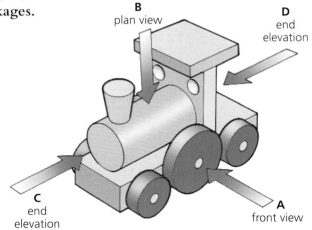

▲ **Fig 1** Views of an object.

Q1 Why are working drawings needed?

These are formal methods of drawings which can be understood by anyone in the world. They are called first-angle projection and third-angle projection. These will have views of the object from all directions; these views are called **elevations**. They are the front elevation, two end elevations and a plan view, which is a view from above.

In Fig 1, the plan view is looking from B, the end elevations are D and C and the front elevation is seen from A. Third-angle projection is now the most commonly used projection, with the end elevations drawn next to the end from which they are viewed. Most objects can be drawn with just three views – one end elevation, a front elevation and a plan view – but you can include others if they are needed. Lines that join points on the various views are lightweight and called construction lines. The actual outlines of the drawing are much heavier.

The orthographic drawings in Fig 2 are coloured to make them clearer. Normally they are just drawn in pencil.

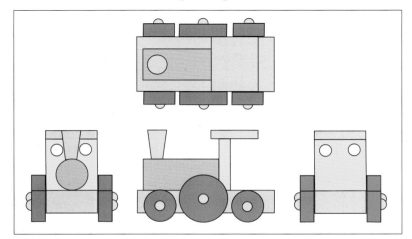

◀ **Fig 2** Third-angle projection.

Sections

Sometimes to show parts which may not be obvious, **sections** are drawn. These show the parts as if they have been cut across (Fig 3). This is like taking a loaf of bread, cutting it and then looking at the cut face. It is often used to show internal parts, joints or construction methods.

You can make these drawings using conventional drawing equipment – you will need a drawing board, a tee square, set squares 30°, 45° and 60°, HB and 2H pencils. However, it is easier to make your drawings using one of the many computer-aided design (**CAD**) packages available, such as *Design View* or *Design Tools*. These will help you to arrange and line up your drawings, and some packages will automatically **dimension** the drawing, as you do it (Fig 4).

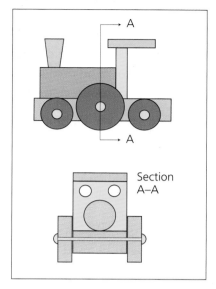

▲ *Fig 3* A section at A–A.

Q2 What are the two types of projection?

Q3 What is a section?

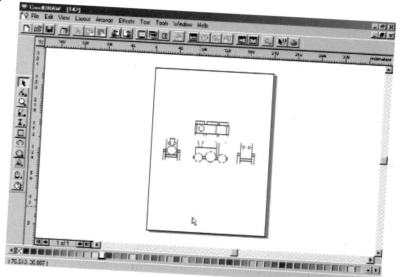

▶ *Fig 4* Computer-aided design.

Key words

CAD – computer–aided design
dimension – add measurements to drawings
elevation – a view
orthographic – drawing using straight lines
section – the view of a cut through an object

SUMMARY

■ Orthographic projection is a scale drawing which has all the information to make an object.

■ There are two styles; first-angle projection and third-angle projection. Each has at least three views, called elevations, of the object.

■ Third-angle projection is the most commonly used projection.

SUMMARY *activity*

Make a quick sketch to show the layout of a drawing in third-angle projection (See Fig 2). Use a simple object such as a toy as an example.

14 Presentation techniques

In this section of the book you will learn the following things:
- how to present your graphics work;
- what methods to use to make the best of your work;
- using computers to enhance to your work.

When you are designing, you should record all of your ideas. The next most important thing is to present your ideas as efficiently and attractively as possible. Remember though that good presentation cannot cover up poor ideas or project development.

Using colour

Colour can be used to good effect but do not overdo it. You can use pencils, pastels, pens and felt-tips to shade your drawings. Just going around the edge of a pencil drawing with a highlighter pen will make it stand out on the page. This is a good idea if you have a page with lots of drawings. You can bring that drawing to the attention of the reader. It is often quite difficult to do a series of good drawings on a page. If you have some good examples, cut them out and paste them onto paper; this is what professional designers do.

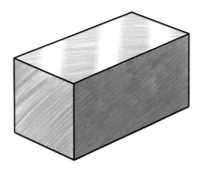

▲ *Fig 1* Shading using colour.

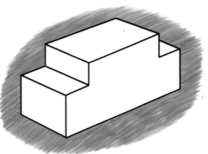

▲ *Fig 2* Highlighting.

This often happens when doing quick development sketches at the beginning of your designing. You might do an excellent quick sketch on paper that has other marks on it – in this case, cut and paste it (Fig 3). Never throw rough drawings away, you can always put them in a clear envelope which can be handed in when your project work is marked. You can also cut and paste photographs that have been taken.

Q1 Why is it important to record all your ideas?

▲ *Fig 3* Cut and paste.

Using CAD and clipart

When using CAD packages, you will be able to cut and paste easily. There is now lots of **'clipart'** available for use. You could also take your own photographs and scan them or use a **digital camera** and **download** the results into your drawing package. This method could help you to record the making of certain parts of your project or the testing of ideas where the model may be damaged or destroyed such as in a structures project.

▲ **Fig 4** Clipart examples.

▼ **Fig 5** A digital camera.

Q2 What is cut and paste?

Q3 What could you use clipart for in your work?

Q4 How could you record the testing of a model structure to put into your graphics work?

Key words

clipart – graphics from CD-ROMs and the Internet which can be added to your work

digital camera – a camera which takes pictures which are stored in digital form

download – to send information to your computer from the Internet or cameras, etc

SUMMARY

- There are many ways of improving your graphics work. Using coloured pens, pencils, felt tips and crayons can give your drawings texture and form.
- When using graphics packages, you can download clipart and photographs into them. You can take your own photographs and scan them, or use digital cameras.

SUMMARY activity

Use a CAD package to produce an A4 sheet explaining how to use clipart and cut and paste techniques.

15 Producing a folio

In this section of the book you will learn the following things:
- the reasons for making folios of your project work;
- the information a folio should contain;
- the use of a technical notebook.

Making your project folio

A project folio should be a record of all of your thinking and decisions. It will show your teacher how you attempted the project.

Q1 Why are folios used in project work?

Your folio should have all or most of the following pages, depending on the materials you are using. If you are doing a food project, then the working drawing might be replaced by a recipe. For textiles, a pattern may be needed.

Front cover – contains your name, project title and course details.

Identification of need – sets the scene, how you found the problem.

▲ **Fig 1** A front cover.

Design brief – a short sentence saying exactly what you are doing.

Specification – the requirements of the project, what it has to have.

Generating ideas – looking at the problem, finding out how it could be done. You could also look at any similar items which may be on sale in shops.

Initial ideas – a small group of ideas from which you will develop your project.

Research and investigation – refining and combining your initial ideas.

Development – developing the chosen ideas, refining all the parts of the project, changing those which do not look good, adjusting sizes and materials. Make sure that everything is recorded. There can be small modification drawings or just written comments by drawings. These will explain your thinking to others.

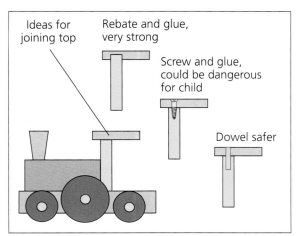

▲ **Fig 2** Development of an idea.

Final ideas – what you are actually going to make, perhaps with small modifications and adjustments.

Pictorial drawings – coloured, three-dimensional drawings which show how your project will actually look, giving others a really good idea of what you are going to make. You could show different colour schemes.

Working drawings – **orthographic drawings** showing how the project is put together, details of the construction and the sizes of the various parts.

Cutting lists – the amounts of materials needed.

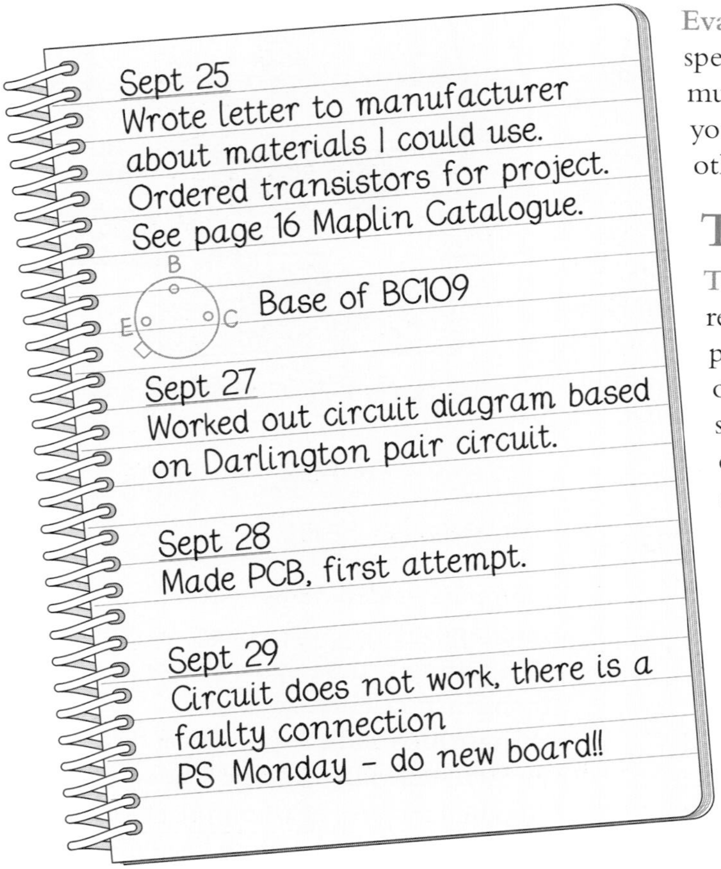

Evaluation – how near to your specification the project is. You must judge it carefully against your proposals. You could also get others to comment.

Technical notebooks

Technical notebooks – used to record the information that you pick up on the technical aspects of your project. It may be the specifications of materials and components or the addresses of suppliers and other sources of information.

◀ **Fig 3** Technical notebook entry.

Sept 25
Wrote letter to manufacturer about materials I could use. Ordered transistors for project. See page 16 Maplin Catalogue.

Base of BC109

Sept 27
Worked out circuit diagram based on Darlington pair circuit.

Sept 28
Made PCB, first attempt.

Sept 29
Circuit does not work, there is a faulty connection
PS Monday – do new board!!

Q2 Why are pictorial drawings needed?

Q3 Why might a technical notebook be necessary?

Key words

orthographic drawing – a style of drawing with measurements and construction details
pictorial drawing – a realistic, rendered drawing of the project
research – finding out information
technical notebook – written comments about technical aspects

SUMMARY
- A folio is a record of your designing.
- It should contain drawings with some written comments.
- The content depends on the materials used, such as textiles, food or resistant materials.

SUMMARY activity
Design a front cover for your latest project.

16 Drawing using computers

In this section of the book you will learn the following things:
- when to use computer-aided design;
- what computer-aided design lets you do;
- what animation is used for.

Computer versus pencil?

Using a computer you can draw really life-like pictures and easily produce good orthographic drawings, but it can take a long time. You must be sure that it is worth spending the time at the computer. Drawing using other methods might be easier and less time consuming. It also helps if you really know the program you are going to use.

The major advantages are that you can save your work to disk and change it at a later date. Once you have entered all the information, you can print it out in a variety of different forms and any number of times (Fig 1). You could even send it to other people over the Internet.

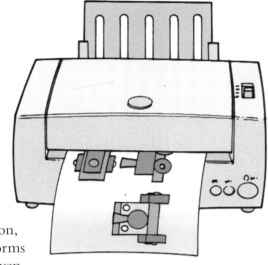

▲ **Fig 1** *Printing out your drawings.*

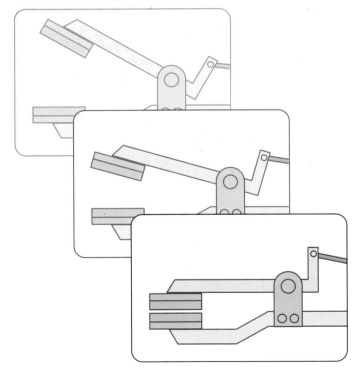

▲ **Fig 2** *A drawing which can be animated.*

Q1 Why use a computer instead of pencil and paper?

Computer-aided design (CAD) **packages** let you do a range of different things from orthographic drawings (constructional drawings with **dimensions** and constructional details) to pictorial drawings (realistic shaded and coloured pictures of your project or parts of it). Sometimes these can be as good as photographs. Some CAD packages allow you to rotate your designs to see how they look from all angles, others let you **animate** drawings (Fig 2). If you have a mechanism with moving parts, you can see how they move in relation to each other. This can be done either in the solid modelling form or as a moving 'orthographic' style drawing.

In Fig 3 you can see a screenshot of Parametric Technology Corporation's *Pro/DESKTOP* package with several different views on the same screen – your school may have this software for you to use.

▼ **Fig 3** Pro/DESKTOP *screen shot.*

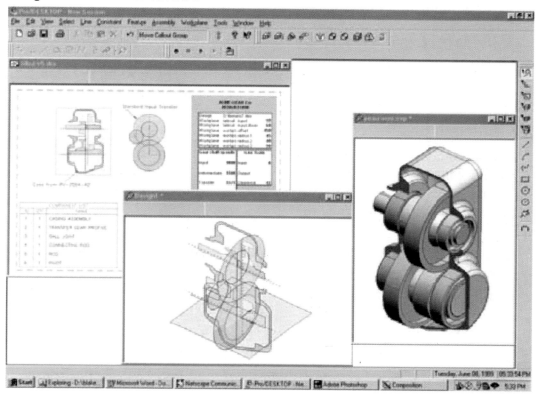

Q2 What are the advantages of rotating a solid model on screen?

Q3 Why would you need to look at moving drawings of mechanisms?

When you have finished your drawings, most CAD packages will produce files that will operate **stencil cutters** or **milling machines** to help you make parts for your project. This is discussed later in the book.

Key words

animate – make drawings appear to move

dimension – measurement

milling machine – a machine which can cut and shape metals, or thick plastics

packages – complete computer programs

stencil cutter – a machine similar to a plotter which can cut card or thin plastic sheet

SUMMARY

■ CAD packages allow you to do a range of different styles of drawings.

■ They will produce a range of orthographic or pictorial styles.

■ Solid models can be rotated and viewed from all angles.

■ Some drawings of mechanisms can be animated to show movement.

SUMMARY activity

Use a CAD package to draw some cylinders and shade them so that they look real.

17 Modelling

In this section of the book you will learn the following things:
- the reasons for modelling;
- that there are many different types of modelling;
- how modelling can help you improve your designs.

What is modelling?

In Design and Technology, there are several different meanings of the word 'modelling' – one is making **scale** models of products, mechanisms or structures (Fig 1). Another meaning is testing out ideas using computers, for example you could model an electronic circuit or a structure to see if it works without actually making it. Changing values in a spreadsheet to see what happens is also modelling.

▲ **Fig 1** Three-dimensional models.

When designing mechanisms, you can cut out card levers and cams and pin them to a board to check if your ideas work satisfactorily. This is two–dimensional modelling (Fig 2).

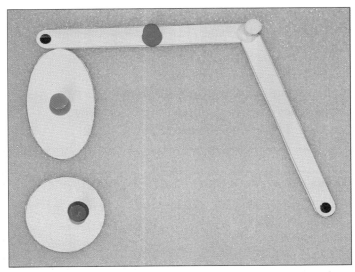

▲ **Fig 2** Two-dimensional model.

There are **kits** such as Fischer Technik and Lego which allow you to easily model mechanisms by clipping parts together.

Testing using modelling

When you make a model, it can help you decide on the **aesthetic** properties of the final product such as its colour, size, shape and feel. It will allow you to adjust areas that you do not like. Your model can be the size of the product or it can be to scale if it would be too large to make, e.g. a model of your school workshop.

Q1 What are the advantages of modelling mechanisms over making them?

▲ **Fig 3** *A simple foam model.*

The model may be of a product which would be too expensive to produce in the real material. Most people can understand a model better than trying to read drawings, though drawings do allow others to see a representation of what you are intending to produce.

Models can be very simple just to check out an idea, e.g. the shape of a controller for a game may be modelled from **polystyrene foam** (Fig 3). This would tell you about the size and shape only. Your model could also be an exact **replica**, e.g. of a meal or a CD player, which could be difficult to tell from the real product (Fig 4).

Q2 Give two reasons for modelling a hand-held games controller.

Q3 Why do architects produce models of shopping malls, airports and buildings?

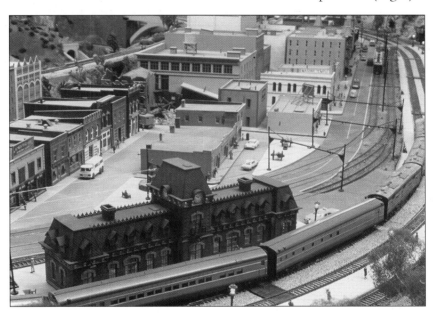

◄ **Fig 4** *An accurate scale model.*

Key words

aesthetics – the tastefulness and artistic beauty of the product

kits – sets of components which clip together easily without tools

polystyrene foam – a plastic material used for modelling

replica – a copy

scale – the size of the model compared to the real thing

SUMMARY

■ Modelling allows you to test out ideas, either by drawing or making representations of things either at actual size or to scale.

■ You can use a computer to model circuits, test structures, change patterns or ingredients.

■ Modelling is useful in showing others, such as teachers or clients, what the finished product will look like.

SUMMARY *activity*

Make a convincing model of a meal, such as a salad, on a paper plate. You can use recycled materials such as coloured polythene sheet from carrier bags, painted polystyrene foam and card.

18 Modelling materials

In this section of the book you will learn the following things:
- the materials which are available for modelling;
- why these materials are used for modelling;
- the need for safety when using these materials.

Modelling materials are chosen because they are easy to cut and shape, and sometimes because their surface texture looks like the finish you are trying to achieve.

Types of modelling materials

'Found' materials are those we would normally throw away, like plastic bottles, old toys and containers. Sometimes their complicated shapes and mechanisms make them very useful.

Card and paper can be used for developments, making up cubes, cylinders and boxes. They come in a range of thicknesses and different surfaces so can be cut into strips and glued together.

Balsa wood is a very light hardwood which is easy to shape and glue together using balsa cement or **PVA** glue.

Modelling clay can be used to create complicated shapes; some types can be baked in an oven to harden them, e.g. Fimo (Fig 1). Some modelling clays are red or grey, others are brightly coloured.

Expanded polystyrene is a foamed plastic which is available in sheets or blocks.

Q1 Why are 'found' materials often good to use for modelling?

▲ *Fig 1* Fimo models.

Q2 How could you model the handle of a screwdriver using modelling clay?

Styrofoam is a fine-celled expanded polystyrene in two grades, blue and white. The blue styrofoam is slightly coarser than the white foam. They can be sanded and worked more easily than other foams (Fig 2).

Styrofoam and expanded **polystyrene** foam can be cut with a hot wire cutter and must be painted with water-based paint.

◄ *Fig 2* Blue and white styrofoam.

Foamed plastics look like sheets of polystyrene but with dull, tough surfaces. Air is blown into it during manufacture, so it is lightweight and easily cut. It is halfway between polystyrene foam and polystyrene sheet and is usually available in bright colours.

Jelutong is a soft **hardwood**, that is really easy to carve and shape. It has a fine grain which allows small details to be formed.

Medium density fibreboard, MDF, is a manufactured board which is very dense – it can be cut and shaped easily. It gives a good surface, especially when sprayed or painted.

Safety

Safety is important when using these materials. Dust from sanding and filing jelutong, MDF and polystyrene can be dangerous to health, so always use face masks and goggles. Use your school's dust extraction system and work close to it. Using a hot wire cutter on polystyrene foam produces **toxic** fumes, so you must ensure that there is adequate ventilation (Fig 3).

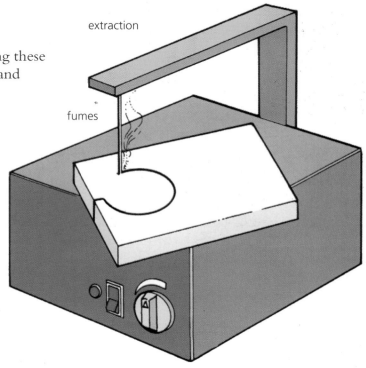

extraction

fumes

▲ **Fig 3** *Always use safety equipment.*

Q3 What precautions should you take when using modelling materials in the workshop?

Key words

hardwood – wood from a tree that loses its leaves in winter
polystyrene – a thermoplastic
PVA – poly vinyl acetate
toxic – dangerous to health

SUMMARY

■ There is a wide range of materials which can be used for modelling.
■ All are used because they are easy to cut and shape.

SUMMARY *activity*

Make as accurate a model as you can of a small chair using 'found' materials.

19 Scale

In this section of the book you will learn the following things:
- why you need to use scale models;
- how to use scale;
- how scale is measured.

▲ *Fig 1* *A small scale model of a house.*

> **Q1** If your model car was 5 cm long, and the real car was 5 metres, what scale is the model?

Measurements

Every measurement of the house would be divided by ten to find the measurements of a model at 1:10. If you wanted to make a larger model of the real thing then you would multiply the measurements instead of dividing.

Sizes

Scale means increasing or decreasing the size of the model compared to the real thing. For instance, if you were making a scale model of a house, you would make it smaller than the house itself. The scale you use will depend on how big you want your model to be. If the real house is ten metres high and you wanted a model one metre high, then the scale would be 1:10. This is a ratio of sizes so there are no units; you can think of it as a fraction. Certain things like model soldiers or cars are made to **fixed scale** such as 1:32, 1:15, 1:12.

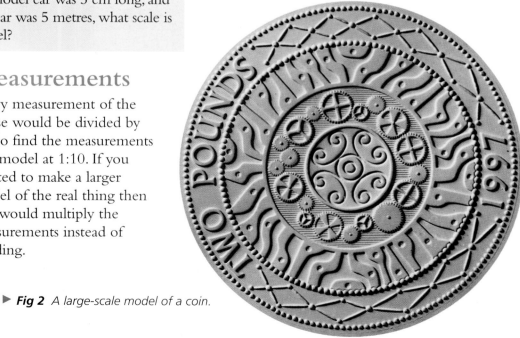

▶ *Fig 2* *A large-scale model of a coin.*

Often when people are designing coins or medals, they make larger models on which to work (Fig 2). This makes it easier for them. The models are often over 25 cm in diameter, whilst the real coin may be only 2.5 cm so the scale is 10:1. When finished, the model's dimensions are reduced by a **pantograph** machine.

A model which is the same size as the object is at a scale of 1:1. Similarly, a drawing which is half the size of the object is to the scale of 1:2.

Q2 Why do coin designers work on a large model of the coin?

Realism

To make your models look **realistic**, it is important to use materials which are in scale. For example you could, in the case of the house, make very good roof tiles from plastic sheet, but you must take care that the plastic sheet is the correct thickness otherwise your tiles may appear too big. The smaller the model, the more difficult it is to make it appear realistic.

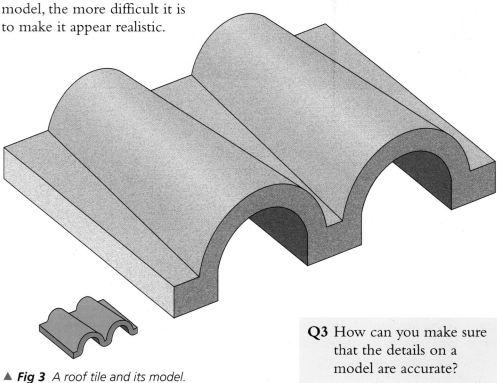

▲ **Fig 3** A roof tile and its model.

Q3 How can you make sure that the details on a model are accurate?

Key words

fixed scale – where things are made to certain scales, such as model trains
pantograph – a machine which reduces or increases measurements
realistic – like the real thing
scale – a ratio of sizes

SUMMARY

■ Scale is used to make an accurate drawing or model which is larger or smaller than the original object.
■ Scale is always given as a ratio, e.g. 2:1.

SUMMARY *activity*

Use card and paper to make a 1:4 scale model of your favourite book or magazine. Colour the covers to look exactly like the original. Use scrap paper to represent the pages.

20 Kits

In this section of the book you will learn the following things:
- how kits will help speed up your modelling;
- the advantages of using kits;
- what types of kits are available for use in school.

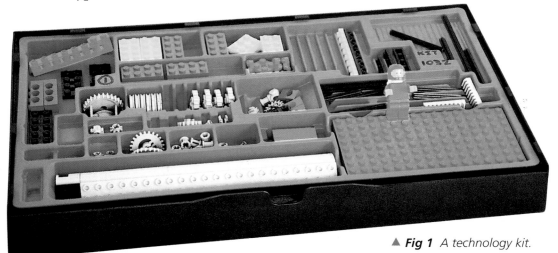

▲ **Fig 1** *A technology kit.*

Using kits

The major advantages of **kits** are that all the components you need are to hand and the parts clip together without the need for tools (Fig 1). Kits are collections of components or materials which allow you to model things or to practise certain skills such as stencilling or batik.

> **Q1** Give one reason for using kits, other than speed and not requiring tools.

▲ **Fig 2** *A modelled mechanism.*

In some kits, all the parts are returned to the box after use, e.g. **mechanisms**, **structures** and **electronics**. In other types, some of the materials, such as paints, dyes and waxes, are used up and will have to be replaced but brushes, containers and instructions remain. In the first type of kit, the main advantages are that you can make structures and mechanisms without drilling and cutting wood, plastic or metal. If you are making a mechanism, you have to do some very accurate measuring and drilling to get it to run freely (Fig 2). With electronic kits, all the components plug into boards so there is no need for soldering, and often small components are mounted on blocks making them easier to handle and preventing damage to their leads. Some parts, such as diodes or transistors, can only be plugged in the correct way round (Fig 3).

Types of kit

Electricity kits have simple switches, buzzers, bells, batteries and motors, and a selection of different coloured leads. These components can be mounted on colour coded blocks with easy connections.

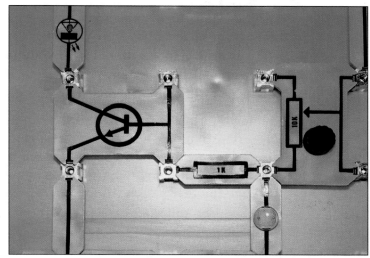

▲ **Fig 3** *An electronic circuit.*

Electronic kits can be very simple, like the electricity kits above, or very complex. Some have prototyping boards and power supplies built in, so that complex circuits using integrated circuits can be tried out.

Q2 If you model a mechanism using a kit and then want to actually make it, what problems could there be?

Q3 Components in electronic kits are often labelled with their names, how can this help you when doing your project?

Pneumatics kits have a range of valves, regulators, actuators and tubing to allow you to construct and model **pneumatic** systems.

Mechanisms kits have gears, pulleys, cams, levers and axles. There are boards with correctly spaced holes for the axles so that gears will mesh accurately.

Structures kits have novel ways of connecting struts together. Sometimes the struts are plastic sections which can be cut to length with a craft knife.

Key words

electric/electronic – using voltage and current to achieve things
kit – group of components to help do a particular task
mechanism – a system of gears, cams, pulleys working together
pneumatic – using compressed air to operate things
structure – the framework of buildings, machines or organisations of people

SUMMARY

■ The purpose of all kits is to let you model a range of activities easily and quickly, usually without the use of tools.
■ There are kits for specific tasks.

SUMMARY activity

Use a kit to make a small rolling vehicle with three wheels.

21 Two-dimensional modelling

In this section of the book you will learn the following things:
- why it is important to model in two dimensions;
- how to model the moving parts of your design;
- how to print, plot or cut out your designs.

Sketching is a form of two-dimensional (2D) modelling. It is attempting to try out ideas using graphics – this could be quick sketches or coloured, **presentation drawings**. However, especially when designing products with moving parts, such as a toy dumper truck, you might want to know where a pivot point is or if one part will miss another part when moved.

Q1 Why is it difficult to tell from a drawing, if the moving parts of a project will hit each other?

You could do accurate **orthographic drawings** and calculate the **pivot points** but this will take time (Fig 1). Using your initial drawings, you can cut out the shape of the parts in card or thin plastic, and experiment with different pivot points using drawing or map pins as pivots.

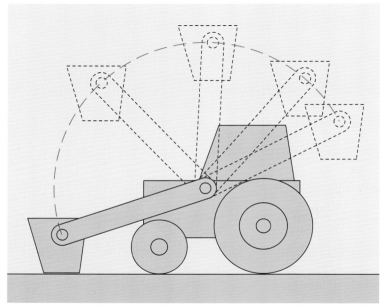

▲ **Fig 1** *Ideas for a project with moving parts.*

▲ **Fig 2** *Map pins, indicator pins, drawing pins.*

You need to choose a board soft enough to take the pins. You can then move the parts to check if they will touch each other. If they do, then change the pivot point (Fig 3). If you do not want to pin your patterns to a board, then you can use paper fasteners (the ones with two legs that bend back).

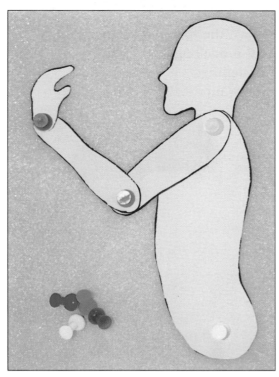

For an even stronger pivot use eyelets – the sort found on belts (Fig 4). If you are already using a **CAD** package to do your drawings, then you can plot out directly onto card. If your school has a **stencil cutter**, then the card can be cut out as well.

One use of this technique is to make an **ergonome**, sometimes called a manikin. This is a 2D scale model of the human body which can be used to test your scale-model products. The measurements of people are found in **anthropometric** data charts. There is a pattern to make an ergonome on page 209.

◀ **Fig 3** *Modelling parts of a project using pins and card.*

◀ **Fig 4** *A flexible joint can be made using eyelets and eyelet pliers.*

Q2 Once you have found the pivot points on the card patterns, how would you transfer them onto your work?

Q3 You have two pieces of card with eyelets in. How could you join them together so that they will turn easily?

Key words

anthropometric – to do with the sizes of human bodies

CAD – computer-aided drawing

ergonome – a scale model of the human body with flexible joints

orthographic drawing – accurate scale drawing

pivot point – a point of rotation

presentation drawings – coloured drawings which show the product as if in 3D

stencil cutter – a plotter which cuts card or plastic sheet

SUMMARY

- Two-dimensional modelling is a good method for trying out ideas.
- It can be quick sketching of your ideas, coloured presentation drawings or using card patterns pinned to boards. This method allows you to check if any moving parts obstruct other parts of your project.

SUMMARY *activity*

Use card and drawing pins to make a model of a pair of scissors.

22 Three-dimensional modelling

In this section of the book you will learn the following things:
- the advantages of three-dimensional modelling;
- which materials can be used for modelling;
- the reasons for using different types of models.

Exploring your ideas

Three-dimensional (3D) modelling is an excellent **visual** way of exploring your ideas and communicating them to others. Everyone seems to understand 3D models better than drawings. Some designers start designing by modelling in card, clay, or styrofoam so that they can quickly explore their ideas (Fig 1).

Q1 Give two reasons why modelling clay is used for exploring ideas.

▲ **Fig 1** A simple clay model.

Models can be very simple for testing just the dimensions, or extremely accurate and **detailed**, and difficult to tell from the real product (Fig 2). Car manufacturers make full-size models of new cars, firstly to see how they look, and then later to take final measurements. Models can be made from shaped and painted polystyrene foam to look like any material. Complicated shapes can be **fabricated** by gluing sheet, tube and block or **found materials** together. They could also be made from the actual material to be used, such as steel, for testing the strength of the proposed product. If you were designing a soft toy, this could be modelled in foam and coloured to look like the real thing. How it is made really depends on what the model is needed for.

◄ **Fig 2** Different types of model.

Modelling the project

Often, it may not be necessary to model the complete product, only those parts which are difficult to resolve. A dress designer may try out a variety of decorative techniques on a dress made from **muslin**, and experiment until a successful solution is found. Then paper patterns can be cut from it, saving the possibility of wasting expensive textiles.

Kits allow models of structures, mechanisms, electronics and pneumatics to be constructed.

A glue gun is a really useful tool in modelling, as well as craft knives, saws, files and abrasive papers (Fig 3).

Q3 Give a reason for only modelling a small part of a project.

Q2 Name three types of toys which are accurate models of the real thing.

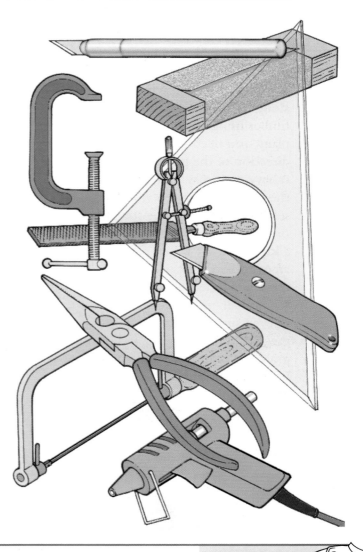

▶ *Fig 3* Tools for model making.

Key words

detailing – putting fine detail on a model such as surface texture or lettering.

fabrication – making up something from materials

found materials – those which we normally throw away (scrap)

muslin – a type of cloth used for modelling

visual – what we see

SUMMARY

- Three-dimensional modelling can be used at any stage of a design process to generate, investigate, develop or modify your ideas.
- Models can be made using any available materials, from found materials to the actual material of the final product.
- They can be simply made to investigate shape and feel, or very accurately made to explore the visual qualities.

SUMMARY *activity*

Use modelling clay to make a full-size model of a nameplate for your bedroom door, no bigger than 100 mm by 40 mm and up to 10 mm thick.

23 Cutting away materials

In this section of the book you will learn the following things:
- how to recognise the grain in timber;
- how to cut timber, metal and plastics;
- how to cut large holes.

The grain in timber

Timber has a grain which runs along its length. If cutting timber using a saw, knife or plane, you need to know the direction of the grain, otherwise it may split. Look at the surface of timber: you will see lines which may be straight or very wavy, especially around a **knot** (Fig 1). When planing an edge, you must plane *with* the grain, otherwise the plane will judder and make an uneven surface. Turning the piece of timber around and planing from the other end will help. When sawing, the grain will not be a problem but care is needed to stop pieces with short grain from breaking off (Fig 2).

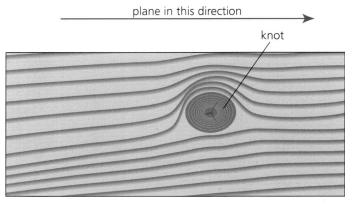

▲ **Fig 1** The grain in timber.

Q1 Why is care needed with short grain?

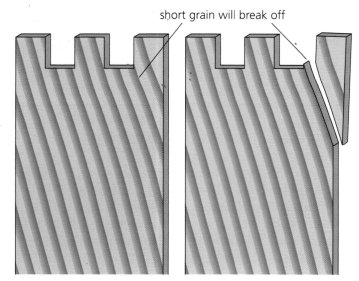

▲ **Fig 2** Short grain.

When drilling timber always put a piece of scrap wood under it to prevent splitting. To prevent splitting when sawing, use a marking knife first on all cut lines.

Metal

Metals do not split or crack when you saw, drill or file them. When drilling always make a centre punch mark to stop the drill skidding on the surface. Clamp the metal down onto a piece of wood. Never attempt to hold small pieces with your fingers – always use a machine vice or clamp (Fig 3).

Plastics

Plastic may split when it is filed, drilled or sawn. When drilling, use a small piece of tape to stop the drill skidding around. Do not press hard on the drill especially when 'breaking through' as this will easily crack the plastic; instead, clamp the plastic to a block of scrap wood.

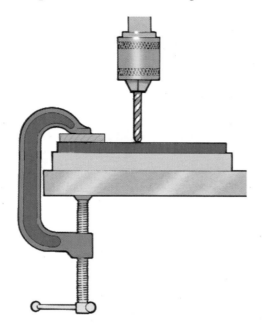

▲ **Fig 3** *Drilling metal or plastic.*

When cutting or filing thin metal or plastic, hold them as close to the vice jaws as possible. Use **soft jaws** to prevent marking the surfaces. Both materials may have very sharp edges after cutting.

Cutting large holes

To cut large holes in all materials, drill a small hole, put the blade from a coping saw for wood, or an **Abrafile** blade for metal, through the hole and then refit the blade in the frame (Fig 4). Files, rasps and surforms can be used to shape the materials and to make them smooth.

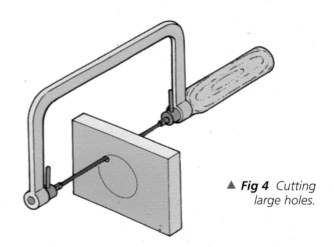

▲ **Fig 4** *Cutting large holes.*

Q2 Why should you clamp materials down when drilling?

Q3 Why do you need to be careful with the edges of plastic or metal?

Key words

Abrafile – a file or blade which will cut in all directions

knot – a round dark part of timber where a branch starts in the tree

soft jaws – soft plastic jaws to fit in a vice to prevent marking the surfaces being held

SUMMARY

- Wood has a grain which may make it difficult to cut; sometimes it will split.
- Plastics and metals need clamping down when drilling.
- Plastic and metal will have sharp edges after cutting.

SUMMARY *activity*

Draw a heart shape on wood 100 mm x 100 mm x 10 mm. Drill a hole near to the inside edge of the heart. Use a coping saw to accurately cut out the shape.

24 Joining by gluing

In this section of the book you will learn the following things:
- how adhesives work;
- how to prepare the materials for joining;
- safety when using adhesives.

Adhesives

Some adhesives will fill gaps between the two materials to be joined and others must have close-fitting joins to be successful. Some need the materials to be **clamped** together for several hours until a good **bond** is made (Fig 1), while others have to be put onto both surfaces and allowed to become tacky before putting the surfaces together. Some glues are waterproof and will stay strong even under water. When gluing smooth surfaces, such as plastics or metal, you need to roughen them slightly, using emery cloth to get a strong join; make sure that there is no grease present.

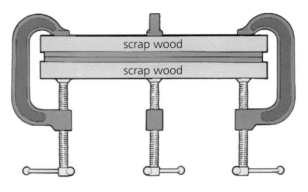

▲ **Fig 1** Clamping materials together.

Q1 Why do materials need clamping together when using some adhesives?

Poly vinyl acetate (PVA) is a general adhesive used in schools, but is not fully waterproof. It can be used for joining wood, paper and card. Joints need to be clamped together for several hours in a warm room.

Resin-based wood adhesives, such as Cascamite, are powders mixed with water to produce a creamy liquid. When dry, the joints are totally waterproof and really strong. The materials need to be clamped together.

Contact adhesives are used to join sheet material such as metals and chipboard. They are thinly spread on both pieces, allowed to dry and then pressed together. The bond is instant – it will be difficult to move either piece (Fig 2).

Rubber-based glues, such as Copydex, stay flexible when dry and can be used to join textiles, paper and card.

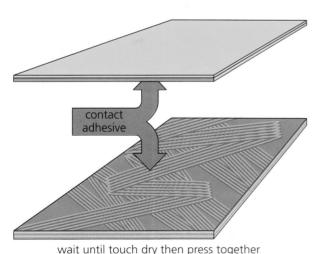

wait until touch dry then press together

▲ **Fig 2** Contact adhesive use.

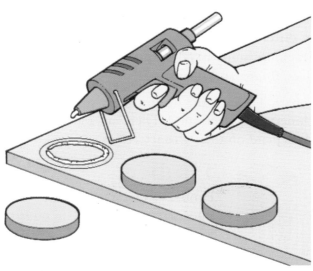

Hot-melt glue guns are great for temporary fixing of most materials. They have a heated nozzle and the glue stick is pushed through it by a trigger. They are good for **tacking** things together quickly. Take care – the hot glue will burn your skin (Fig 3).

Perspex cement is a **solvent** which slightly melts plastic. Do not get it anywhere else, as it will mark the plastic badly – use tape to keep the glue off the plastic. The joins must be very close fitting.

▲ **Fig 3** Using a hot-melt glue gun.

Safety

Many adhesives have dangerous chemicals and solvents in them so they must be used in well-ventilated areas. You must use goggles and aprons, and make sure you do not get them on your skin (Fig 4).

▶ **Fig 4** Ensure good ventilation when using adhesives.

Q2 What type of glue would you use to build a small boat?

Q3 Why is it important to be careful when using adhesives?

Key words

bond – joining together using glue

clamping – forcing two materials together using a G-clamp or vice

solvent – chemical which dissolves others

tacking – temporary gluing

SUMMARY

- There are many different types of adhesive which are designed to do different jobs.
- Some are waterproof; some are for particular materials while others are for general use.
- Safety is very important when using them.

SUMMARY activity

Join small pieces of wood or plastics together using different glues. When they are dry, hang weights on them to test which glue is strongest.

25 Permanently joining materials

In this section of the book you will learn the following things:
- materials can be joined in many different ways;
- wood can be joined using interlocking joints fixed by glues;
- metals can be joined using solders, fluxes and heat.

Permanent joins are not easily taken apart. They are the mechanically strong joints that you find in furniture, machinery and electronics. There are a lot of different ways to join materials which depend on their characteristics.

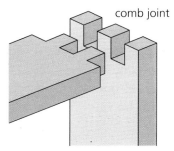
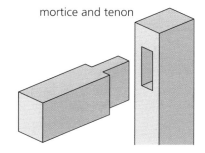

▲ **Fig 1** Joints in wood.

Timber

Timber can be fixed together using glues, screws or nails. The most common joints used in wood are mortice and tenon, dovetail and finger joint (Fig 1). These rely on the mechanical strength of the joint which is fixed into place using glue. The joints are cut using back saws, coping saws and chisels. When screws or nails are used to join timber, you are relying often on their shear strength and not on any mechanical help from the timber itself (Fig 2).

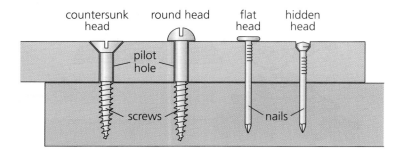

◄ **Fig 2** Screws and nails.

Metals

Metals can be joined by soft or hard soldering, brazing or welding. Soft solder is an alloy of lead and tin and melts at a low temperature. A soldering iron or gas torch is used to melt the solder. Soldering is used for joining electronic components together (Fig 3). Hard or silver soldering uses a gas torch as the temperature is much higher, and is used for jewellery and small, strong joints (Fig 4).

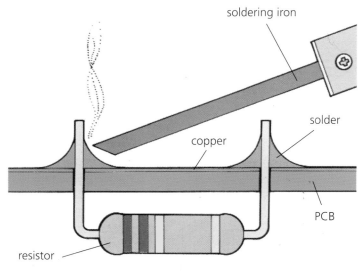

▲ **Fig 3** Soldering electronic components.

Brazing uses **spelter** and a much higher temperature for really strong joints in metals. When soldering and brazing, the metals need to be very clean and the joints tight fitting; **flux** should be used to stop the metal from **oxidising** during heating.

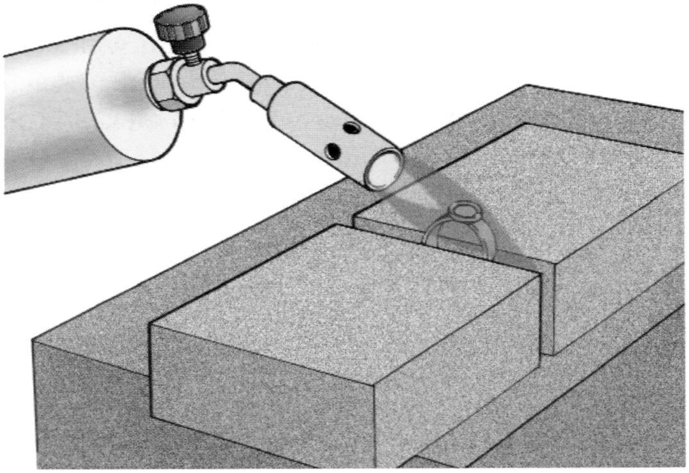

Plastics

Plastics can be joined using solvents which melt them. The joints have to be tight fitting for maximum strength.

▲ **Fig 5** *Rivets and washers.*

▲ **Fig 4** *Silver soldering.*

Rivets are made from soft metal and are hammered into a mushroom shape using tools called sets and snaps. Pop rivets are hollow rivets which are put in using a pop riveter which pulls the rivet up tight and then breaks off. These are useful for joining panels where you have access to only one side (Fig 5).

Different materials can be permanently joined together. Glues are available which will join almost any materials together.

Q1 Why are joints like dovetails used in furniture?

Q2 Why are fluxes used when soldering or brazing metal?

Q3 How could you join plastic and metal together permanently?

Key words

brazing – a high temperature join using spelter

flux – a paste which stops oxygen from affecting metals when heated

oxidising – oxides forming when metal is heated

spelter – a brass used for brazing

SUMMARY

■ Some joins rely on the strength of the materials.

■ Glues can just lock the joints together. Screws and nuts and bolts can join different materials together.

■ Metals can be either soldered, brazed or welded using heat, depending on their types.

SUMMARY activity

Use thick card to make a small model of a finger or comb joint as shown in Fig 1.

26 Temporary joining of materials

In this section of the book you will learn the following things:

- how materials are joined so that they can be taken apart;
- using templates which are tacked in place;
- why knock-down fittings are used.

Temporary fixing allows things to be assembled and taken apart easily. Sometimes they are used to hold templates whilst marking out and cutting materials.

Plastics, metals and sometimes wood can be joined using nuts and bolts. Holes must be drilled in both pieces to allow the bolt to be fitted. Washers will prevent the head of the screw being pulled into softer materials. If you are drilling several holes, drill the first then put the nut and bolt in and drill another, then repeat (Fig 1).

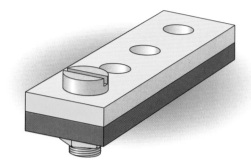

▲ **Fig 1** *Drilling a number of holes.*

> **Q1** Why are washers sometimes used when joining softer materials?

Screws and nails are normally permanent fixings, but they can be used to hold patterns against timber being marked and cut out. You can use them to hold work together until the glue dries and then remove. This is called **tacking**. Any holes can be filled in (Fig 2).

Halving joints can be used to make things which can be easily taken apart. Each piece has slots which slide together, and support each other (Fig 3).

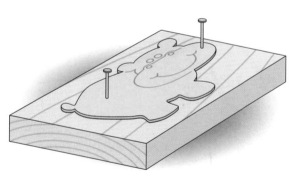

▲ **Fig 2** *Tacking using nails.*

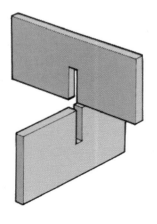

◀ **Fig 3** *Halving joints.*

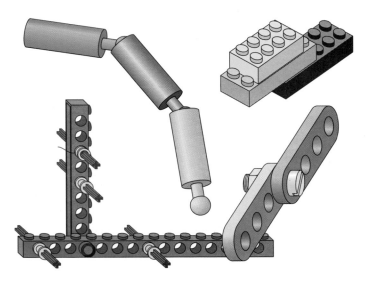

▲ **Fig 4** *Joints from kits.*

Movable pieces such as those in toys and doors have catches, hinges or pivots which can be considered as temporary fixings. They allow the parts to be fixed together and still move. Jigsaws and construction kits are examples; the jigsaw links pieces together using shapes, while construction kits use a lot of different methods to provide very strong joints. You should look at the ways used to join the parts of the kits – you may be able to use the idea in your projects (Fig 4).

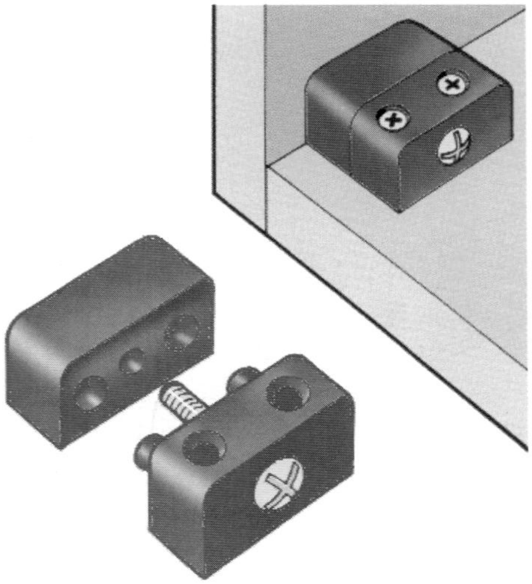

Velcro is used for the temporary fixing of textiles, it has a surface of tiny hooks on one part and loops on the other part. When pressed together, a reasonably strong connection is made. Velcro can also be glued to resistant materials to provide temporary joins and is useful for toy construction.

Knock-down (KD) fittings are available for use in **flat-pack furniture**; they allow joins in materials to be easily made using only a screwdriver (Fig 5).

▲ **Fig 5** *A flat-pack joint.*

Q2 What does a temporary joint allow you to do?

Q3 How does velcro work?

Key words

flat-pack furniture – furniture that you assemble yourself
halving joints – joints having similar but opposite slots cut into each piece
tacking – using nails as a temporary fixing
velcro – a textile joining tape

SUMMARY

■ Temporary fixings allow things to be taken apart.
■ They can be used to hold materials in place whilst cutting or drilling.
■ Kits are good examples of the use of temporary fittings.
■ Knock-down fittings are used to make furniture easily.

SUMMARY *activity*

Use the idea in Fig 3 to design an animal shape made of thin plywood or thick card. The body should be about 120 mm x 80 mm and the legs from two pieces 100 mm x 60 mm.

27 Finishing techniques

In this section of the book you will learn the following things:
- why finishing is necessary;
- how to finish different materials;
- what finishing means in food and textiles.

Surface finishes

Finishes usually protect a surface against moisture, heat or dirt and dust. A poor surface finish cannot be covered up by paint as any marks will look even worse when painted.

Getting a good finish on timber starts with good planing, then a scraper can be used. Use different grades of **abrasive papers**, wrapped around a sanding block. Always sand with the grain otherwise scratches will show up when polished (Fig 1). Wire wool can be used after the wood has been dampened with a cloth. This will make it swell slightly and raise the grain. When dry, rub again with wire wool, and repeat until a good surface is obtained. This surface can be wax polished, varnished or painted. A few light coats are better than one heavy one. It is a good idea to finish the wood before final assembly (Fig 2).

Q1 Why are finishes necessary, especially on wood?

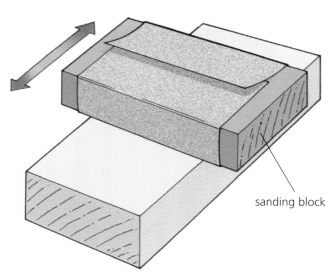

▲ **Fig 1** *Sanding along the grain with a sanding block.*

sanding block

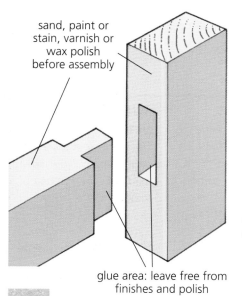

sand, paint or stain, varnish or wax polish before assembly

glue area: leave free from finishes and polish

◀ **Fig 2** *Finishing before assembly.*

Plastic sheet usually only requires the cut edges to be polished but care is needed not to scratch the surface. Leave on any protective paper and use soft jaws on the vice. The edges should be draw filed (Fig 3) until all marks are removed, then wrap emery cloth around the file and continue until smooth.

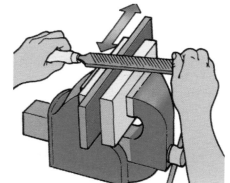

▶ **Fig 3** *Draw filing.*

Using a tightly wrapped cloth, rub on perspex polish. Wipe clean with a new cloth for a shiny surface. To speed up the process, a **buffing machine** can be used with care, but do not press too hard or you may melt the plastic (Fig 4).

Q2 Why are soft jaws required when holding plastics in a vice?

Q3 Why should you not press hard when using a buffing machine to polish plastics?

▲ *Fig 4* *Using a buffing machine.*

Metals can be treated the same way as plastics, using files and emery cloth. Use the emery cloth with oil for final finishing. The buffing machine can also be used. Metals can be painted after any grease has been removed.

Textiles and food

In textiles work, finishing can mean tidying up seams and adding final decoration or it can mean finishes applied to textiles to make them fire or water proof or to improve their wear characteristics.

In food, finishing usually refers to making the product look pleasing by adding food **glazes**, **garnishes** and sauces.

Key words

abrasive papers – sand, garnet, emery papers used to smooth surfaces

buffing machine – an electric motor with rotary mops

garnish – to decorate food using colours, textures, etc

glaze – a coating of egg, sugar solution or stock to provide a shine on food

SUMMARY

- Finishing is used to protect materials from humidity, heat or corrosion.
- It is also used to make materials look attractive.
- Care should be taken not to mark materials when holding them in the vice.
- When using a buffing machine use full safety equipment.

SUMMARY *activity*

Cut out a small shape in acrylic sheet. Try to finish the edges to match the surface finish.

28 Making one-off products

In this section of the book you will learn the following things:
- why prototypes are made;
- the problems of only making one-offs;
- why writing an evaluation is important.

Prototypes and mock-ups

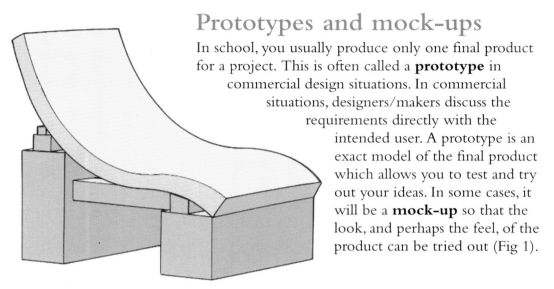

In school, you usually produce only one final product for a project. This is often called a **prototype** in commercial design situations. In commercial situations, designers/makers discuss the requirements directly with the intended user. A prototype is an exact model of the final product which allows you to test and try out your ideas. In some cases, it will be a **mock-up** so that the look, and perhaps the feel, of the product can be tried out (Fig 1).

▲ **Fig 1** A mock-up.

In other cases, it will be the real thing which can be used fully. This first prototype allows information to be found out about all aspects of its design and manufacture. Alterations and modifications can be made; if any parts are unsatisfactory, these can be changed and another prototype can be produced (Fig 2). Clothes could be modelled in inexpensive textiles to establish the look and fit then, when all the problem areas are sorted out, made using the real, more costly materials.

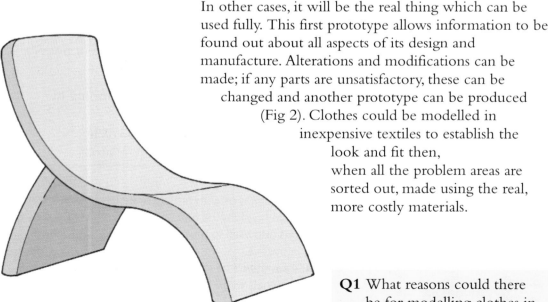

▲ **Fig 2** A prototype.

Q1 What reasons could there be for modelling clothes in cheap textiles?

Checking your ideas

When you are working on your project, you must try to reduce the chances of problems at the making stage. This can be done by modelling and testing your ideas throughout; this takes the place of a real prototype. In a sense it might be more difficult to make a one-off, as you have to make it work first time. When you make more than one, you have some experience to call on as you make them – you can learn from your mistakes and improve the techniques used.

▲ *Fig 3* *A user testing a model.*

Evaluation

Your project should be made as well as you can possibly make it. Any aspect that you are not satisfied with can be **evaluated**. You should write down the reasons why you are not satisfied and how you would improve it. It should also satisfy the needs of the person or persons for whom you have designed it – they should help to evaluate it also (Fig 3).

Q2 Why should you let someone else evaluate your product?

Q3 Why do you usually produce only one product when making in school?

Key words

evaluate – to compare with the specification
mock up – a model
prototype – a first model

SUMMARY

- One-off products are usually made by craftspersons.
- The user can discuss their needs directly with the designer/maker.
- Your projects may have to be successful first time, so evaluation by yourself and/or the intended user is really important.

SUMMARY *activity*

Use modelling foam to make a mock-up of a small pocket torch. Make it look as realistic as you can.

29 Making more than one product

In this section of the book you will learn the following things:
- what mass, continuous and batch production are;
- how CAD can be used to produce multiple copies;
- how to organise the batch production team.

Methods of making

There are advantages in making large numbers of products. The **raw materials** are cheaper the more you buy. The technique is called continuous or **mass production**. Most supermarket products are made by this process. You might be asked to work in teams, perhaps, to produce a number of products. This might be food, e.g. biscuits or cakes for a party or parents' evening, or badges or T-shirts for a school club.

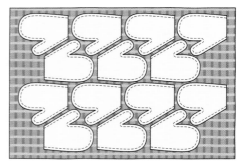

▲ **Fig 1** Using cut and paste to produce multiple copies of oven gloves.

When you make your product, you will need to cut out lots of identical things. You can use a CAD package to design the shapes needed and to duplicate them using the copy or cut and paste functions. If you have sheets of plastic, card or pastry, you can then arrange them so that you get the most items on a sheet, with little waste. You could cut out plastic or card materials using a stencil cutter. With food, you could make up a pastry cutter to cut out several shapes with one cut. With textiles, you could arrange patterns to make the most economical use of the materials (Fig 1).

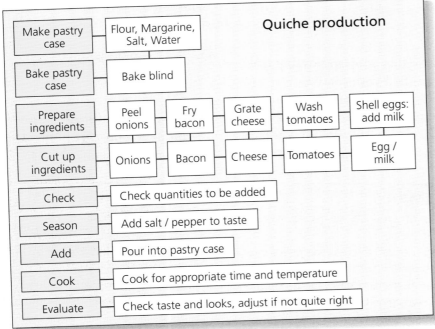

▲ **Fig 2** A block diagram for a food system.

Q1 How can you use CAD to make lots of copies of the shapes needed?

Another method is called **batch production**. It has some of the advantages of mass production but is done on a smaller scale. The method of production will need to be broken down into tasks. You will have to organise groups of people and find out how to order and use the raw materials efficiently (Fig 2).

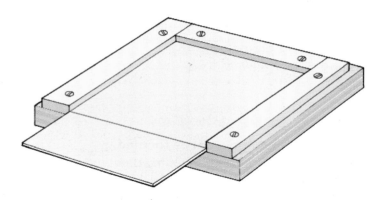

▲ **Fig 3** *Using a jig to fold card accurately.*

You will need to design the system and split your team into management, production management, costing, stock control, production line, **quality assurance** and sales (if you have enough people). You may have to design and make **jigs** to help you measure, cut and bend or assemble your project accurately (Fig 3). You could use a **flow chart** or block diagram to show how the system is to be managed (Fig 4).

Choosing the people

Title	Name	Reason chosen
Manager	Jenni	Good organiser
Product manager	Tony	Understands how things work
Costing	Sue	Good at maths
Stock control	Will	Neat and organised
Production line	Jim	Gets on well with group
Quality assurance	Dianne	Analytical
Sales	Sophie	Pleasant personality

Q2 Why might you need a jig?

Q3 Why is batch production used in schools?

◀ **Fig 4** *The responsibilities.*

Key words

batch production – making small quantities of products

flow chart – shows the organisation of a project

jig – pattern which helps you assemble your project

mass production – making very large quantities of products

quality assurance – making sure products are up to standard

raw materials – basic materials used to make things

SUMMARY

- Mass produced goods are made in large quantities. Making large numbers reduces the costs.
- Batch production is used for smaller quantities. The production must be divided up into stages.
- Systems must ensure that the product is of good quality.

SUMMARY *activity*

A small greetings card has a gold foil 'Hello' and some line decoration drawn on the front. Design a flow diagram to show how it could be batch produced by several pupils.

30 Forming materials

In this section of the book you will learn the following things:
- simple ways to form wood, metal and plastics;
- the use of formers for shaping;
- casting molten metals.

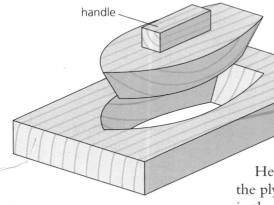

handle

▲ **Fig 1** Simple forming of plastics.

Forming plastics

Thermoplastics can be **formed** by heating and pressing them into a **mould**. Small model masks and badge shapes can be simply cut out of timber: place your pattern on the plywood and draw round it remembering to add the thickness of the plastic all around. Cut out the shape. Heat the plastic, then use drawing pins to fix it to the ply **former** and press the pattern through the hole in the plywood and hold until cool. You can use food containers for the thin plastic (Fig 1).

You will also have a vacuum forming machine in school. The softened plastic is pulled onto the pattern using suction. The pattern will need to be smooth as all marks will show up. Remove the protective sheet from the plastic before use.

Thermoplastics can be heated in an oven and held onto a former until cooled. The former can be cut out using a jigsaw. Line the former with thin card to stop the grain marking the plastic (Fig 2).

Forming other materials

Timber and plywood can be bent using steam; they will need clamping, as with the plastics process, until they cool and dry out. **Laminating** is gluing up layers of wood or plastic around a former, and holding them in place until the glue sets. Complicated shapes can be made by this method. Layers of light and dark materials will look very attractive and can be filed or cut to shape (Fig 3).

Q1 What is a plastic called which can be softened by heating?

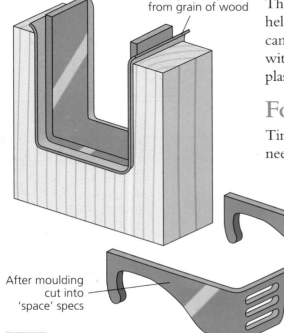

Thin card to protect plastic from grain of wood

After moulding cut into 'space' specs

◄ **Fig 2** Using a former to bend plastics.

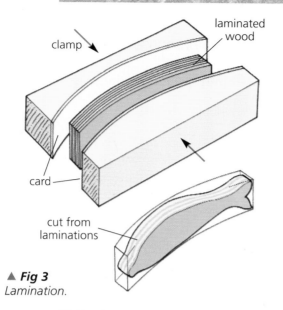

▲ **Fig 3**
Lamination.

Most metals can be heated and hammered into shapes. Thin metals, especially copper and brass, can be beaten into bowl shapes and the surface can be **planished**, which is hammering on a metal stake. This puts small dents into its surface and gives a textured and decorative surface (Fig 4). Metals can be melted and **cast** by pouring into permanent moulds or sand moulds. When cooled the moulds are opened and the solid metal product can be taken out and polished (Fig 5). This is often used for making jewellery.

Q2 Why is a card liner needed when using heated plastic in a former?

Q3 What happens to metal when it is cast?

▼ **Fig 4** Planishing.

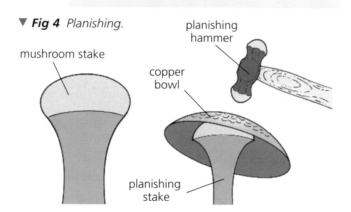

▼ **Fig 5** Casting.

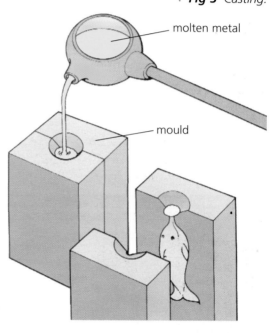

Key words

casting – pouring molten metal into a mould
formed – shaped
former – a pattern around which materials can be shaped
laminating – gluing together thin strips of material to make a thicker one
mould – molten metal is poured into this to make a shape
planishing – hammering the surface of sheet metal

SUMMARY

- Forming is bending and shaping materials.
- Wood can be laminated into shapes using a former.
- Metal can be heated and beaten into shape or melted and poured into moulds.
- Plastics can be heated and formed into shapes.

SUMMARY activity

Make a small former as in Fig 3 from wood or modelling foam. Glue together different coloured card to make up a laminate. When it is dry, cut it into an attractive shape.

31 Computer-aided manufacturing

In this section of the book you will learn the following things:
- how computer-aided manufacture can be used in school;
- the types of work that can be done using computer-aided manufacturing;
- making accurate multiple copies.

CAD/CAM

Computer-aided manufacture (**CAM**) means designing things using a **CAD** package and then loading your designs into a CAM machine. Sometimes pieces of equipment, such as knitting or embroidery machines, plug directly into a computer. Some equipment needs the disk containing the instructions to be loaded into the **stand-alone** machine (Fig 1).

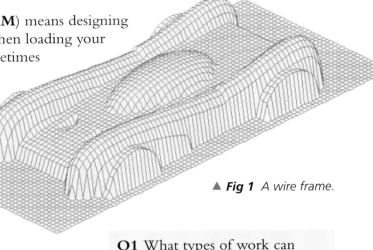

▲ **Fig 1** A wire frame.

Q1 What types of work can CAM machines do?

▼ **Fig 2** An embroidery pattern.

Embroidery software such as *Poem* (Fig 2) enables you to design badges and embroidery panels in colours and different stitch forms, and then to output them to specialised sewing machines which will reproduce them in detail.

Patterns can be downloaded into knitting machines, and these will reproduce your designs. The knitting can then be sewn into finished garments or hangings.

Stencil cutters

Stencil cutters cut card and thin plastic sheet. So you can make card models with folds and cuts, badges, patterns or **templates**. To make folds in card, two drawing files can be made: one for the outline and the other for fold lines. Some stencil cutters let you set the pressure on the knife so a light cut can be used for the fold lines and a heavier cut made for the outlines. Sometimes, just making the folds as dotted lines will be enough.

Milling machines (Fig 3) have rotary shaped cutters and can cut out accurate three-dimensional shapes in metal or plastics. Some will copy shapes by use of a probe which transfers information to the computer and the files can then be modified on screen. To prove your design, wax blocks are often used instead of cutting the metal or plastic. Because the wax is very soft, no damage will come to the milling machine or its cutters should a faulty move be made. Some machines are designed to cut away the copper sheet on printed circuit boards instead of using chemical etching.

▲ **Fig 3** A milling machine.

Q2 Why are wax blocks used to test milling machine program files?

Q3 How can you save materials by using CAM?

CAM is very useful when making identical multiple copies for batch production. It will help you to make the most use of raw materials, by letting you fit the various parts closely together and then producing them very accurately (Fig 4).

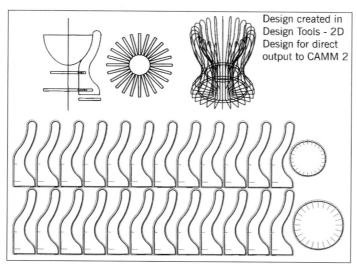

Design created in Design Tools - 2D Design for direct output to CAMM 2

◀ **Fig 4** Repeating patterns.

Key words

CAD – computer-aided design
CAM – computer-aided manufacture
stand-alone – self-contained, does not need to be connected to anything else
template – a pattern, used to draw around

SUMMARY

- CAM allows designs to be cut out of card and plastics, milled out of metal, embroidered using silks or knitted.
- Once designed, the parts or patterns can be reproduced any number of times very accurately.

SUMMARY activity

Design a net for a card box to hold ten computer disks.

32 Selection of materials

In this section of the book you will learn the following things:
- what type of choices there are to make;
- selecting the properties which you need;
- the possible effects of your choices.

Making a choice

When selecting materials, ingredients or components, you have a wide choice from which to choose. There are two main groups: **resistant materials** such as wood, metal and plastics and **compliant materials** such as textiles and paper. You must choose by looking at their **properties** to see if they match your needs. These can be physical properties such as strength, texture or appearance or chemical properties such as containing carbohydrates, proteins or iron.

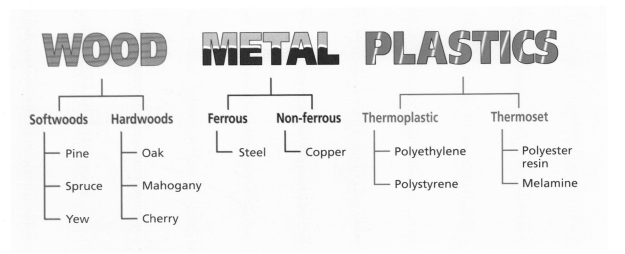

▲ **Fig 1** Choices of types of materials.

> **Q1** What properties might be needed for the materials for a child's sit-on toy?

After choosing a material or ingredient for your project, you must look at exactly which type of that material you need. For example, if you choose to use plastics, which type will you use? Often, the choice will be a compromise and you will want one specific **characteristic**, e.g. strength, look, smell or taste. This one characteristic may decide which one to use, and perhaps make its other characteristics less important to you (Fig 1).

Material limitations

Choose to use a material only if you have the equipment to work it in school. It is no use selecting one which you cannot cut or manipulate. Similarly, selecting a material which is not readily available can cause you problems – you may have to use another instead.

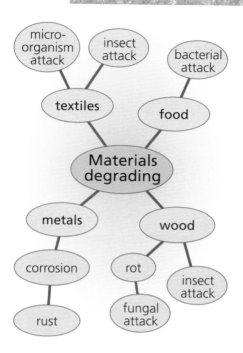

▲ **Fig 2** Degrading of materials.

Most materials **degrade** with time: wood rots, metal rusts and corrodes, textiles break down and food may become rancid or unsafe to eat. This has to be taken into consideration.

You must ask how long your project has to last. It may be a garden tool which will need to be around for years or a food project lasting only a few hours before it is eaten. A design brief might be to design food to be used in a survival pack for astronauts, so it may have to last for many months.

The environment

Can the materials used in your project be recycled when it is no longer required? You should think of using materials which can be easily recycled and which come from renewable sources.

▶ **Fig 3** Recycling.

Textiles: recycled into new fabrics

Food: any waste food/plant material can be composted

Metals: melted down for aluminium cans, etc.

Wood: converted to woodchip and made into other products

Plastics: recycled into other plastic items e.g. fence posts, fleece material

Q2 What are three characteristics of the ingredients needed for a salad?

Q3 Why do you need to know about how long a material will last?

Key words

characteristics – the qualities of a material or ingredient

compliant materials – textiles, paper

degrade – to break down or rot

properties – the characteristics of a material or ingredient

resistant materials – wood, metal and plastics

SUMMARY

- There are many materials and ingredients to choose from.
- They all have their own characteristics.
- You may select, based on just one characteristic. Sometimes you have to compromise.
- Try to use materials which are recyclable.

SUMMARY activity

Write down three ingredients of a salad in a chart and give the physical characteristics of each and why they are used.

33 Timber

In this section of the book you will learn the following things:
- how to identify the different types of trees;
- the difference between softwoods and hardwoods;
- how trees grow.

Softwoods and hardwoods

There are two main types of timber or wood: softwoods and hardwoods. The names have nothing to do with how hard or soft the wood may be, but with the type of tree from which it comes.

Softwoods come from **coniferous** trees, also called **evergreens**, because they keep their leaves in winter. The leaves are also spiny and waxy (Fig 1). The trees are generally triangular in shape and they grow very quickly, reaching maturity in ten to 30 years (Fig 2).

Q1 Are hardwoods harder than softwoods?

▼ **Fig 1** The leaves of a coniferous tree.

▶ **Fig 2** A coniferous tree.

▼ **Fig 3** The leaves of a deciduous tree.

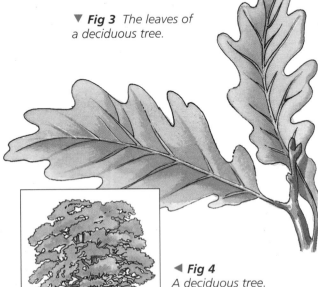

◀ **Fig 4** A deciduous tree.

Hardwoods come from **deciduous** trees which lose their leaves in winter. The leaves on these trees are broad and flat (Fig 3). The trees are generally rounded in shape like a cloud and are slow growing; they take about 100 years to reach maturity (Fig 4).

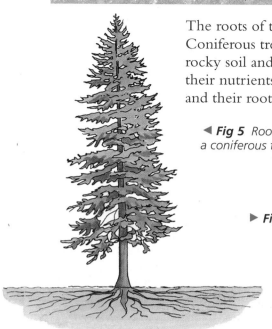

The roots of the two types of tree are also different. Coniferous trees have shallow roots because they grow on rocky soil and need to spread out near the surface to get their nutrients. Deciduous trees grow best in good soil and their roots go deep.

◀ **Fig 5** *Root spread of a coniferous tree.*

▶ **Fig 6** *Root spread of a deciduous tree.*

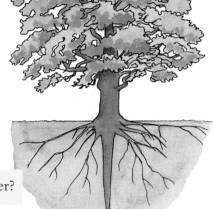

Q2 How do the roots of deciduous and coniferous trees differ?

The cost of timber

If a tree takes a long time to grow, its timber will be more expensive than that of a fast growing tree. Trees which grow in tropical forests where there is high humidity will grow faster than those in this country. It is important to keep as much of our forests and jungles as possible; plants and trees help to extract the carbon dioxide from our air and replace it with oxygen. The roots of the trees take up water and nutrients from the soil, which move up the tree in the form of sap. The water and the carbon dioxide in the air are converted into food by the action of light on the leaves and oxygen is given off. This process is called **photosynthesis**.

Q3 How do trees help the atmosphere?

Key words

coniferous – tree which has cones; usually an evergreen

deciduous – tree which loses its leaves in winter; broad leafed

evergreen – tree which keeps its leaves in winter; spiny leafed

hardwood – wood from a tree which loses its leaves in winter

photosynthesis – the process in plants of making glucose by using energy from the sun

softwood – wood from a tree which keeps its leaves in winter

SUMMARY

■ There are two main groups of trees: deciduous and coniferous.

■ Deciduous trees produce hardwoods and coniferous trees produce softwoods.

■ Hardwoods are generally more expensive than softwoods because they take longer to mature.

SUMMARY *activity*

Take ten small pieces of different types of timber and identify them. Glue them to a piece of white card, name them and draw an outline of the shape of tree that they come from.

34 Timber conversion and seasoning

In this section of the book you will learn the following things:

■ how and why timber is cut into useful sizes;
■ how and why timber is seasoned;
■ the advantages of air and kiln drying.

Conversion is cutting the timber into useful sizes. There are two methods. The first and cheapest method is sawing the log into boards and called through and through (Fig 1). The advantage is that you get very wide boards, but they tend to **warp** easily.

The second method is quarter sawn (Fig 2). It is more expensive because it takes time, and there is more waste. The advantage is that the timber's grain will show up well when polished.

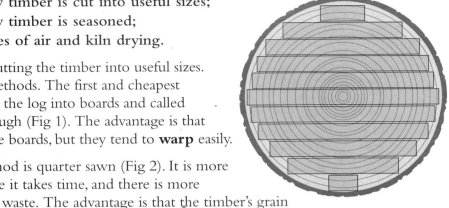

▲ **Fig 1** Through and through sawn timber.

Q1 What is conversion?

When cut down, timber has a lot of moisture in it and is known as **green timber**. If we used it to make furniture, it would crack and split when brought indoors as the moisture would reduce unevenly. The timber must have the moisture content reduced to a similar level to where it is to be used. The process is called **seasoning** and there are two methods.

▲ **Fig 2** Quarter sawn timber.

Air drying

The timber is stacked with spaces for air to flow between the boards. A roof stops the rain from falling on the timber. The timber is raised up on brick pillars to stop rain splashing it and the ends are painted to stop water entering. It is left to dry for several years. Although this method is not expensive, the timber can be affected by insect or fungus attack and some may have to be thrown away. The moisture content can only be as low as the surrounding air, so it may not be suitable for some jobs.

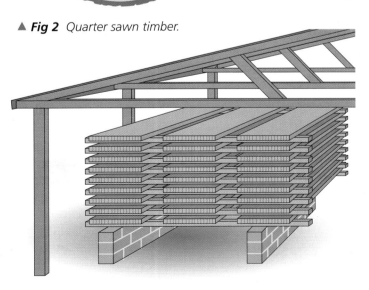

▲ **Fig 3** Air drying timber.

Kiln drying

The timber is stacked, but in a closed building called a kiln which has steam pipes, heaters and fans. Heat is moved around the timber by fans, reducing the moisture content depending upon how much heat and steam are used. It takes only several weeks to get the correct level but can be expensive in fuel and labour costs. Little timber is wasted due to insect or fungal attack. The major advantage is that the moisture content can be accurately controlled.

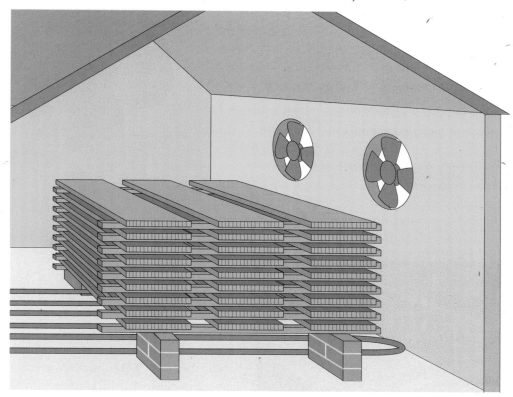

▲ **Fig 4** Kiln drying timber.

Q2 Why is timber seasoned? Give two reasons.

Q3 Why is timber quarter sawn?

Key words

green timber – newly felled timber containing a lot of moisture
conversion – cutting timber into useful sizes
seasoning – reducing the moisture content of timber
warp – twist or distort

SUMMARY

- Before use, timber has to be sawn into sizes appropriate for the building and furniture-making industries.
- It also has to be seasoned to reduce the moisture content, if not, it will split, warp and distort when brought indoors.

SUMMARY activity

Make a small model of timber being air dried.

35 Metals

In this section of the book you will learn the following things:
- where metals are found;
- how to identify ferrous and non-ferrous metals;
- how metals are processed.

Metals occur naturally in the ground either as **ores** or the metals themselves. Ores are rocks which have to be processed by crushing and heating to release the metals. Copper and aluminium ores need vast quantities of electricity to produce the metals. Gold is sometimes washed out of the rocks by rivers and streams. There are gold deposits in this country.

Different metals have different properties; when you are deciding which to use you have to consider which properties you need. If you are making jewellery, you could choose gold, silver or pewter. If these are too expensive, then think about using copper or aluminium or, even cheaper, recycle a drinks can. When designers choose metals, they make a whole range of decisions including cost, wear, strength and safety.

▲ *Fig 1* *Panning for gold.*

◀ *Fig 2* *Scrap ferrous metals.*

Ferrous metals

Ferrous metals contain iron (Fig 2), and corrode or rust when outdoors unless they are painted or surface treated. They are usually magnetic – this is a good test for ferrous metals. When recycling cans, you can separate steel from aluminium by using a magnet.

Q1 How could you test a metal to see if it is non-ferrous?

Q2 Give a reason why aluminium is used for drink cans.

Iron is smelted by heating the ore with coke and limestone in a furnace in a continuous process. This results in pig iron which has lots of impurities. The pig iron is then converted into steel in a Bessemer Converter or Electric Arc Furnace which reduces the impurities (Fig 3). The steel produced is called **mild steel**. Other chemicals such as **carbon**, chromium and vanadium are added to produce different types of steel with differing characteristics.

▲ **Fig 3** Melting metals.

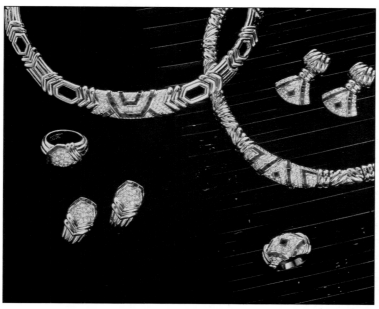

▲ **Fig 4** Articles made from non-ferrous metals.

Non-ferrous metals

Non-ferrous metals do not contain iron and all are non-magnetic. Some examples are copper, aluminium, silver and gold. **Precious metals** such as platinum, gold and silver are valued because they are quite rare and are beautiful. They do not corrode as much as ferrous metal. Gold treasure which has been brought up from shipwrecks is as bright as the day the ship was sunk.

Q3 Why is silver often used for jewellery?

Key words

carbon steel – steel with carbon added; can be tempered
mild steel – a general engineering steel
ore – a rock containing metal compounds
precious metals – rare metals such as gold, silver and platinum

SUMMARY

■ Ferrous metals are usually magnetic and contain iron. They rust when oxygen and water are present.
■ Non-ferrous metals do not contain iron. They are non-magnetic.
■ Precious metals are all non-ferrous. They are usually rare and expensive. They generally do not corrode.

SUMMARY activity

Find four things at home which are made from different metals. Draw each one and say why the metal was used for that item.

36 Changing a metal's characteristics

In this section of the book you will learn the following things:
- how to temper and anneal metals;
- why alloys are used;
- why it is important to recycle metals.

Tempering

Carbon steels can be made to be very hard so that they can be used for springs, knives, chisels and files. They are heated to bright red and cooled in water or oil (Fig 1). They are then polished and heated again to the required colour. A colour chart will tell you what the properties of the steel will be when cooled.

▲ **Fig 1** Tempering steel.

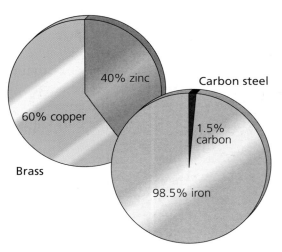

▲ **Fig 2** The composition of some alloys.

Brass
60% copper
40% zinc

Carbon steel
1.5% carbon
98.5% iron

Alloys

The pure metals are not used often but are mixed with other metals to improve their characteristics. Aluminium is seldom pure aluminium but is mixed with copper to make it harder and easier to work. Aluminium is often **extruded** to make long complex shapes such as those used for window frames. If copper is added to the aluminium, it will flow better. Steel is mixed with chromium or vanadium to stop it rusting or with carbon to make it springy or very hard. This process is called **alloying**.

Q1 What is an advantage of alloying metals?

Annealing

When metals are hammered or bent a lot, most gradually get harder and more difficult to work. This is called **work hardening**. To make the metal soft again and easy to work, it needs to be **annealed**. Some, like copper, are heated to red heat and **quenched** in water; others, like carbon steel, are heated to bright red and then left to cool very slowly.

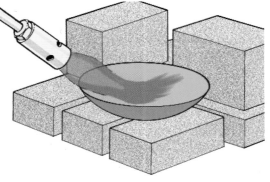

▲ **Fig 3** Annealing a copper bowl using a gas torch on fire bricks.

Q2 What is work hardening?

Q3 How can carbon steel be annealed?

▲ **Fig 4** Recycled metal.

Recycling

It is important that we recycle as much metal as possible for three reasons. The first is that we should not waste natural resources; once they are used up, there are no more. Secondly, producing the metal in the first place uses vast quantities of energy such as electricity, whereas recycling waste metals can use relatively small amounts of energy. Thirdly, there are problems in throwing away materials into landfill sites.

Key words

alloys – a mixture of two or more metals
annealing – making metal softer and easier to work
extrude – squeeze through a die (like a cake icing bag)
quenching – cooling hot metal in water or oil
tempering – heat treating
work hardening – when hammered or bent a lot of metals get harder to work

SUMMARY

- Metals work harden when hammered or bent. They can be annealed to make them easier to work.
- To make carbon steels very hard or even brittle, they can be heated and quenched.
- Alloys are a mixture of two or more metals to change their characteristics.

SUMMARY *activity*

Take a large paper clip and bend it backwards and forwards lots of times. It will get more difficult to bend and may even snap. This is work hardening.

37 Plastics

In this section of the book you will learn the following things:
- how to identify the two basic types of plastics;
- how plastics are manufactured;
- how plastic products are manufactured;
- how to use plastics for school projects.

The types of plastics

Plastics are made from oil. The molecules in plastic materials are arranged in very long chains. The process of producing these long chains is called polymerisation. The individual links are called **monomers**, and the long chains are called **polymers** and are made up of carbon and hydrogen atoms (Fig 1). This gives plastics their flexibility and strength. They are divided into two main groups called thermoplastics and thermosets.

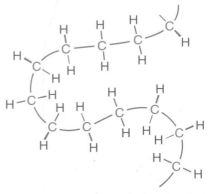

▲ **Fig 1** Long molecular chains.

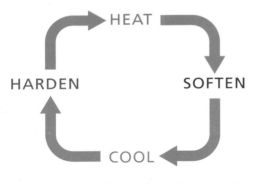

▲ **Fig 2** Thermoplastic heating cycle.

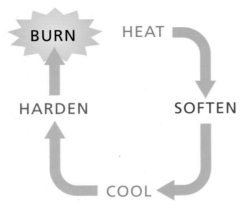

▲ **Fig 3** Thermoset heating cycle.

Thermoplastics are heated during manufacture, and heated again to shape them. They are used for cheaper disposable items such as food containers, crisp packets, squash bottles and plant pots. You probably know that if you heat a plastic bottle or a crisp packet, they will shrink and try to go back to the shape they were before manufacture. This is called **plastic memory** (Fig 2). Some typical thermoplastics are poly vinyl chloride, acrylic and polyethylene.

Thermosets are plastics which are heated and moulded during manufacture. Once cooled down they will not soften any more when heated (Fig 3). If they are heated too much, they just burn. They are used for more expensive things, such as electrical fittings, lamp holders, switches and motor parts. Some types of thermosets are polyester resin, melamine and bakelite.

Q1 How would you tell if a plastic was a thermoplastic or thermoset?

Q2 From which plastic are most bottles made?

The names of some plastics can be confusing. For example you may see a plastic called Polythene which is a trade name; its correct chemical name is polyethylene.

Identification

Plastics are difficult to identify, because they can be any colour, any shape and any texture. The main way to identify them is to do a few tests. You could try to float them on water to see which floats or sinks, saw them and see what the dust does or drop them onto a hard surface to see what type of noise it makes. Some tests suggest that you burn samples to see the colours of the flames and smoke. These tests are very dangerous as plastics give off fumes which are lethal. **Do not try this test!**

Manufacture

Plastics are usually supplied as powders or grains which are fed into machines and heated until they melt. This liquid is then forced through nozzles to make shapes – this is called extrusion. Sometimes the molten plastic is forced into patterns or moulds – this is called injection moulding. Tubes of plastic sheet can be forced by hot air into moulds to produce plastic bottles – this is called blow moulding. At school you will use another process called vacuum forming. This means you will heat a sheet of plastic and suck it over a pattern using a vacuum. Sheets of plastic can be bent using a line bender; this is an electrical element which gets red hot. The plastic is put accurately over the line and softened. At the right temperature, the plastic can be bent, but will need to be held still until it cools. If you do not wait, it will return to its original shape.

> **Q3** What characteristics are needed for the plastic used for lemonade bottles?

Key words

monomers – the smallest part of a plastic material

plastic memory – when reheated thermoplastics try to return to their previous shape

polymer – a molecule formed when monomers are joined together

thermoplastics – plastics which soften when heated, harden when cooled and can be heated and softened again many times

thermosets – plastics which after being heated and softened during manufacture, cannot be changed or softened by heating again

SUMMARY

- Plastics are made from oil.
- There are two main types: thermoplastics and thermosets.
- Plastics can be difficult to identify, because they can be made with almost any surface finish, colour or flexibility. Sometimes different types can be mixed or joined together to produce special characteristics; this also makes recycling more difficult.
- Simple tests can help you identify some of the common ones.
- They are not generally biodegradable, this means that when they are thrown away, they do not rot.
- Plastics are generally difficult to recycle, although most are marked with the recycling logo and their type.

SUMMARY activity

On most plastic items such as lids, food containers and some toys you will find the recycling logo together with some letters such as LDPE. This means low density poly ethylene – the type of plastic from which the item is made. Collect as many items as you can and use a glue gun to fix them to a piece of card. To save space cut out the small piece with the name on. Write out their names in full.

38 Manufactured boards

In this section of the book you will learn the following things:
- why manufactured boards are used instead of solid timber;
- how manufactured boards are made;
- the major uses of manufactured boards.

Natural or man-made?

The problem with natural timber is that it is not usually available in large flat sheets. When it is, it may warp and crack unless very well seasoned. The cost may be high as old mature trees may be used and it may take many hours to join the pieces.

Manufactured boards are made by gluing smaller pieces or thin sheets of wood together to make large sheets. Often the materials used are waste products from the timber industry or from trees which are too small to be used for any other purpose. The surface of the boards can be made to look like real wood by using **laminates** or **veneers**.

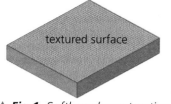

▲ *Fig 1* Softboard construction.

Softboard is usually about one centimetre thick and is made from fine fibres of wood (Fig 1). It is like a soft thick cardboard and is used for notice-boards and partitioning in offices.

Hardboard can be from six millimetres to about 12 millimetres thick. It is made from wood fibres which have been sprayed with glue and pressed between heated plates until dry. It has a smooth, shiny surface on one side and a rough one on the other (Fig 2). It is used mainly for door panels.

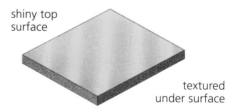

▲ *Fig 2* Hardboard construction.

▲ *Fig 3* Medium density fibreboard construction.

MDF (medium density fibreboard) is a very strong type of board similar to hardboard but much denser. Both surfaces are very shiny (Fig 3). It cuts and shapes easily, and takes polishes and paints very well. It does not split and is used mainly for furniture making.

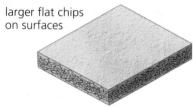

▲ *Fig 4* Chipboard construction.

Chipboard is made from compressed and glued wood chips. The wood chips are usually larger on the outside than the inside to provide a really flat surface (Fig 4). It is very strong when dry but if it gets wet, it swells and falls apart. It is used for kitchen tops where strength is important. The surface is usually covered with a thermosetting plastic. The plastic protects the wood from water. The plastic laminate can also be colour printed with designs which can look like stone or wood and have a **texture.**

Blockboard is a board which is made from square strips of softwood glued together. The surface on each side is covered by a thin sheet of plywood (Fig 5). This makes a very strong and rigid board often used for shelving.

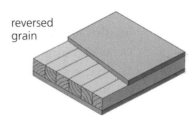

reversed grain

▲ **Fig 5** Blockboard construction.

Laminboard is similar to blockboard but the strips inside are much smaller (Fig 6). This makes a very strong sheet of wood and the surface is very flat. It is used for drawing boards where the flatness is important. It is much more expensive than blockboard.

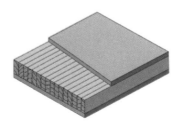

▲ **Fig 6** Laminboard construction.

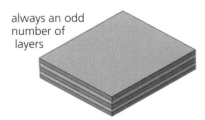

always an odd number of layers

▲ **Fig 7** Plywood construction.

Plywood is made of thin sheets of wood glued together in layers. There is always an odd number of layers, e.g. three, five, seven or nine. The grain of each layer is at right angles to the next, so with odd numbers of plys, the directions of the grain of the two outside layers are always the same (Fig 7). Sometimes, one or both of the outside layers are made from good quality wood such as oak, to give the impression of solid wood. Most plywoods are glued together using waterproof glues but there are some for outdoor use or boatbuilding called WBP, water boil proof. These will not come apart if they get wet.

There is a form of plywood called Stoutheart, which has a thick inner ply. This is generally cheaper and is used for building purposes. Plywood is used for a wide range of things such as building, boat building, furniture making and model making.

Safety

When using any manufactured boards, you must use eye protection and face masks. The dust from both the wood and the glues used to join them can be very dangerous if breathed in.

Q1 Why are manufactured boards useful?

Q2 Which boards are waterproof?

Q3 Where are you likely to find the most chipboard in your house?

Key words

laminate – a thin plastic sheet glued onto wood to protect it

texture – a surface finish which can feel like wood or stone

veneer – a very thin sheet of wood shaved from a large piece of wood

SUMMARY

- Manufactured boards enable us to have large sheets of timber which will not warp, twist or split.
- They often use waste products, or poor quality timber.
- There are many types, all with specific uses. Some are waterproof, and some are not. They often have laminates glued to them.

SUMMARY activity

Cut some narrow strips of thin plywood: two with the outer grain running the length of the strip and two with the grain running across the length.
Test them to see if both pieces are as strong as each other along their length. What happens?

39 Composites

In this section of the book you will learn the following things:
- why composite materials are used;
- that there are very common composite materials all around us;
- how composite materials are made.

Composites are made from a mixture of materials. Each material has some advantage which it gives to the **composite**, such as flexibility, strength, lightness or toughness. Some composites are so strong that they can be used for bullet-proof clothing and aircraft parts, though in fact they contain plastics.

Concrete is a mixture of cement and gravel which is much tougher and harder wearing than just the cement itself. Sometimes concrete has steel rods put in to give even greater strength – this is called steel reinforced concrete (Fig 1). These rods are usually stretched while the concrete sets, to pre-stress it and increase resistance to bending.

▲ **Fig 1** *Pre-stressed concrete.*

Q1 Where do you often see steel reinforced concrete?

Glass reinforced plastics (**GRP**) are composed of a plastic material – polyester resin – which is brittle on its own, into which glass fibres and cloths are mixed. The cloths or fibres are usually laid into a pattern or mould and liquid resin is painted on. When the resin sets, the resulting material can be very thin yet very strong and not easily damaged. Aircraft parts, boat hulls, car bodies and furniture can be made in this way (Fig 2).

▲ **Fig 2** *Boat hulls made from GRP.*

▲ *Fig 3* *A spacesuit made of composite materials.*

Carbon fibre is similar to GRP, but the glass fibres are replaced by carbon fibres or matting which is then baked in an oven to **cure** it. This produces a material that is much stronger than steel yet many times lighter. It is so strong that helicopter rotor blades can be made from it.

Some textiles can also be considered as composites. These are usually a mixture of natural and **synthetic** materials, such as cotton and polyester, which each have very specific **characteristics**. For example, they are comfortable to wear, lightweight and machine washable. In the space industry composite materials are used for many things, including spacesuits (Fig 3).

Q2 Why is glass fibre or carbon fibre put into polyester resins?

Q3 What advantage could there be in making aircraft parts from composites instead of metal?

Key words

carbon fibre – a resin with carbon threads in it

characteristics – the qualities of a material or ingredient

composite – a mixture of two or more materials

curing – heating a resin to set it

GRP – glass reinforced plastics sometimes called glass fibre

synthetic – a material that does not come from a natural source

SUMMARY

■ Composite materials are usually strong, lightweight replacements for more common materials.

■ The characteristics of each material contributes to the new material.

SUMMARY *activity*

Cut a piece of cotton material from an old shirt or clean handkerchief about ten centimetres square. Rub in PVA glue until the cloth is soaked right through. Drape it over an upside down plastic cup. When dry, test how strong it is compared to the cloth itself. This is a simple example of how glass fibre cloth works.

40 Smart materials

In this section of the book you will learn the following things:

■ what smart materials are;
■ what smart materials can and will be able to do;
■ the names of a range of common smart materials.

New materials

Smart materials are a new range of materials which can be controlled by some type of input. Imagine clothes that can change colour with body heat or be controlled by electrical signals, aircraft wings that change their shape with electronic signals and car bodies that will alter their stiffness in a crash. There are computers being developed which are so small, they could be woven into clothes and be undetectable. These are a few things that smart materials are being developed for at the present time (Fig 1).

One type of smart material, called **piezoelectric**, is already used in lighters and microphones. When vibrated, the material produces a voltage. In the case of the gas lighter (Fig 2), it produces enough voltage when twisted to light the gas. In the microphone, the vibrations produce small voltages which can then be amplified. In the future, very small particles will be put into the concrete of buildings and bridges, which will send signals to sensors if the material is going to fail or degrade.

▲ *Fig 1* Smart materials man.

▲ *Fig 2* A piezoelectric gas lighter.

Signs that use electrically sensitive plastics and inks will be used to produce very thin displays which could cover buildings and vehicles. Thus the colour of your car, bus, aeroplane or building could be changed electronically (Fig 3). They could even have moving pictures on them.

Ceramic smart materials can be built into skis which change shape when different vibrations occur. This would make the skiers' ride smoother. Similarly, electroceramics could be built into aircraft to reduce vibrations – especially important in helicopters.

Shape Memory Alloys (**SMA**) are metals, usually **nickel** and **titanium**, that return to their original shape when heated. For example, if your glasses were made of this metal and you dropped them in the playground and someone stepped on them and bent them, then gently heating them would return them to their original shape without damage.

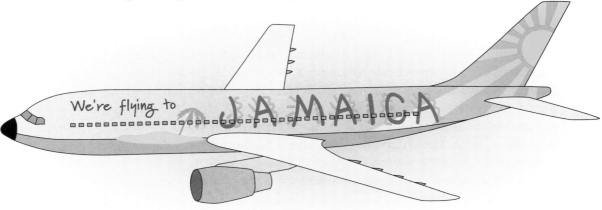

▲ **Fig 3** *Smart materials will eventually give changing colour displays on aircraft, vans, etc.*

Q1 A thin wire of SMA can produce a strong pull over a short distance. How could you use this movement in a model sign display?

Q2 What uses can you think of for very thin displays?

Q3 What advantages are there for knowing if the material of bridges is getting weak?

These alloys are already available for use in school projects. If the metal wire is bent into a spring shape and heated by running an electrical current through it, it will straighten. This movement can be used to operate some part of a design project. For example, it could pull open a lock or be used in a robot arm.

Key words

ceramic – a material made from clay

nickel – a metal

piezoelectric – a material which changes shape if a voltage is applied, and produces a voltage if twisted or struck

SMA – Shape Metal Alloy

titanium – a hard metal

SUMMARY

- Smart materials react to an input and then change some of their properties automatically.
- They will enable a whole range of new engineering and computing projects to be developed.
- Some are already in use in schools and can help you solve a number of design challenges.

SUMMARY *activity*

Design and draw a small card toy which could use the pulling movement of an SMA to make a part or parts move.

41 Measuring and marking out

In this section of the book you will learn the following things:
- accurate marking and measuring can save time and money;
- different methods are used for resistant and compliant materials;
- the tools used for marking out.

Saving time and money

For good making, you will need to measure and mark out your materials very accurately. Good preparation will help you to produce good projects and prevent you wasting too many materials. Having to throw away materials and start again can lose you a lot of time. With resistant materials, the tools used depend on the surface to be marked. Some surfaces like plastics and metal can be marked using scribers and dividers, others like wood need either pencils or marking knives. Some waterproof pens can leave marks on plastics which cannot be removed. Textiles should be marked using chalk – sometimes small cuts or stitches show where pieces are to be joined together.

Q1 Why is accurate marking out necessary when making things?

Tools

Steel rules have accurate divisions marked on them; the best have the measurements cut into the surface. You can then put the points of dividers into these marks to help in transferring measurements.

Straight edges can be used to either draw lines or to cut against.

Tape measures can be used if long measurements are to be made (Fig 1).

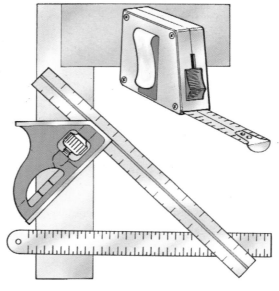

▲ **Fig 1** Straight edge, ruler and tape measure.

Dividers are used to mark out circles or arcs and for transferring measurements from rules to your work. If you need a lot of equally spaced marks, then you can set the dividers to the measurement and step them off (Fig 2).

Callipers are used to measure the internal and external diameters of tubular materials.

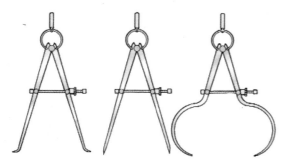

▲ **Fig 2** Dividers and calipers.

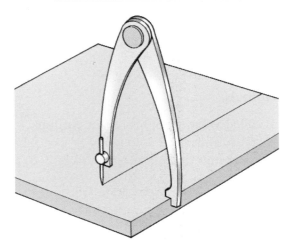

▲ **Fig 3** Using odd legs.

Oddleg callipers are used to draw lines parallel to a straight edge (Fig 3).

Engineers' squares or tri-squares, help you to get materials square by providing an accurate 90° angle (Fig 4).

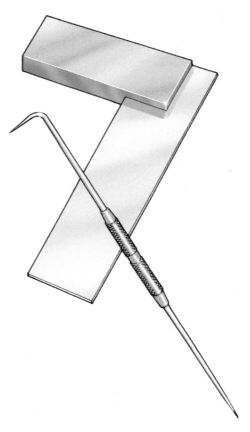

Scribers are **hardened** metal and are used to scratch lines on metal or plastic. To make the lines show up, a **dye** called **engineers' blue** can be wiped onto metal. Only use scribers on plastics if you are going to cut to the mark – do not use where you are going to **heat bend** it, as it will break at the line.

Q2 When should scribers not be used to mark plastics?

Q3 What methods are there for marking textiles?

▲ **Fig 4** Engineers' square and scriber.

Key words

dye – a chemical colour
engineers' blue – a dye used on metal to show marking
hardened – heat treated steel
heat bending – using heat on thermoplastics

SUMMARY

- It is important to measure and mark out your materials accurately. This could save you time and money.
- Plastics and metal can be marked using scribers or pens. Engineers' blue is wiped onto metal to let you see the scriber marks more clearly.
- Wood needs soft pencils or marking knives and textiles require chalk.

SUMMARY *activity*

Mark out and cut six squares of thin card 100 mm by 100 mm. If cut accurately, you should be able to tape them to form a complete box.

42 Cutting and shaping tools

In this section of the book you will learn the following things:
- how to shape different materials;
- what the various tools are used for;
- which tools can be used with which materials.

You can make shapes in materials by a process called **wastage**. This means cutting pieces off using a variety of different tools. Sharp tools must be used safely as accidents can happen so easily. There are useful drawings of hand tools on page 210.

Q1 Why must sharp tools be used carefully?

Cutting

▲ **Fig 1** *Craft knife, scissors and chisel.*

Craft knives will cut paper, card, textiles, timber and thin plastic sheet. They must be used with great care – when cutting always try to use a safety straight edge (Fig 1).

Scissors will cut textiles, paper and card. They can have special edges which will produce decorative cuts. Pinking shears are used to prevent textiles fraying.

Chisels will cut wood. They have a narrow blade to cut slots and joints in timber. Some can be hit with a mallet and have shock absorbing washers fitted. Wood carving tools are small versions of chisels.

Sawing

Back saws are used to cut straight, accurate lines and joints in timber. They have a solid back on the blade and come in different sizes. The largest is a panel saw, then they go down in size to the tenon, then the dovetail and then the gents saws.

Coping saws can cut curved shapes in timber and thin plastics. The blade should be fitted so that it cuts on the back stroke.

Hacksaws are used to cut plastics and metals; a junior hacksaw is a smaller version (Fig 2).

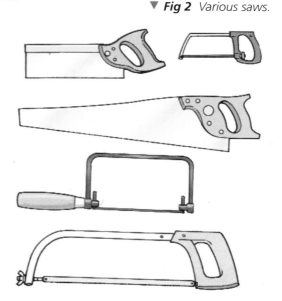

▼ **Fig 2** *Various saws.*

Sanding

Sanding sticks are shaped wooden strips with **abrasive** paper glued onto them. They are used to remove small quantities of wood or plastic. They can be made to suit the shape of the work.

Filing

Files come in many sizes and shapes e.g. triangular, round and flat. There are three different grades: bastard, second and smooth. Needle files are very small and are used for jewellery work.

Rasps are files used for shaping wood. Some, called rifflers, have shaped and curved ends.

Surforms have thin metal serrated blades. They remove lots of timber very quickly and are used for carving (Fig 3).

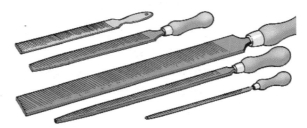

▲ *Fig 3* *Types of files.*

Q2 Why do we need different grades of files and sandpaper?

Q3 Why are surforms often used for carving wood?

Planing

Planes are useful for removing thin shavings of wood to make timber smooth and square. There are many types: jack, smoothing, shoulder, bull-nosed and plough. Spokeshaves are small two-handed planes (Fig 4).

▲ *Fig 4* *Planes.*

Power tools

Power tools will do all of the jobs above, but much faster (Fig 5).

▶ *Fig 5* *Power tools.*

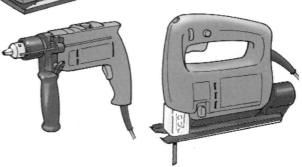

Key words

abrasive – a material which can wear others away

power tools – tools which use electric power

wastage – shaping by removing materials

SUMMARY

■ Wastage is shaping by removing materials, i.e. by cutting pieces off.

■ Tools are used to do this in a variety of ways. Some wear away materials by abrasion; others cut like saws, knives and scissors.

SUMMARY *activity*

Mark out your initial on a 6 mm acrylic sheet. Using a saw and files, cut out and finish the shape accurately.

43 Tools for drilling and cutting holes

In this section of the book you will learn the following things:
- the different methods of cutting holes;
- what the different drills are used for;
- stopping the drill from skidding when drilling.

Drilling holes is a useful way of removing materials and making **pilot holes** for axles, screws, nails and dowels. Hand drills are used for drilling holes and are powered by turning a handle. Power drills use electricity to drive them – they can be held in the hand or fitted on a stand as **pillar drills**. You can do heavier work using a pillar drill (Fig 1).

> **Q1** Why can you do heavier work when using a pillar drill?

The chuck is the part of a drill which holds the drill bit. It is usually tightened up using a chuck key.

A twist drill is a small hardened metal rod with a spiral groove and a ground angled point. It is used for cutting metal, plastic and timber. The smaller the diameter, the faster the drill must turn.

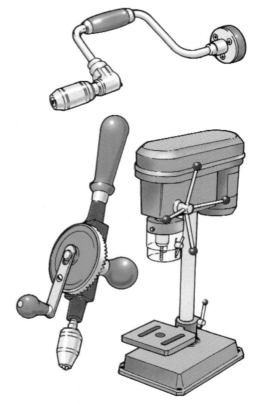

▲ **Fig 1** A hand drill and a pillar drill.

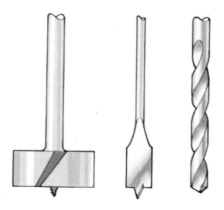

▲ **Fig 2** Forstner, flat and twist drills.

Forstner bits cut smooth, straight, flat bottomed holes. They can be used in power drills and can be large diameters. You can cut overlapping holes with them.

A centre bit or flat drill is used for cutting holes in timber. It has a point which digs into the timber and two arms near the point; one marks the timber and the other cuts away the wood. The holes are rough and not very straight (Fig 2).

Punches are tubes of metal with sharpened edges and are used to punch holes in leather, card, paper and textiles. They are used with a hammer. The materials should be put on a block of wood to prevent damage (Fig 3).

▼ **Fig 3**
Punching leather.

A centre punch makes a small mark on metal so that the drill does not skid across the surface of the metal. It makes sure that the drill is in the correct place. When drilling plastic, put a small piece of masking tape where the hole is to be drilled. This will stop the point of the drill from sliding (Fig 4).

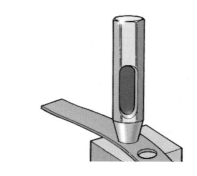

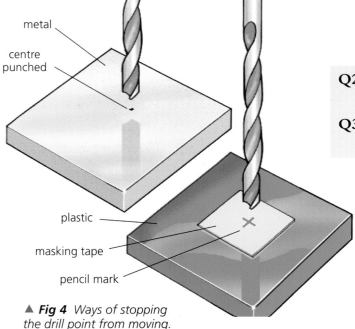

metal

centre
punched

plastic

masking tape

pencil mark

▲ **Fig 4** *Ways of stopping the drill point from moving.*

Q2 What type of bit would you use to drill a flat bottomed hole in timber?

Q3 Why do you need to centre punch metal before drilling it?

Key words

pillar drill – a drill on a stand
pilot hole – a small hole used to stop materials splitting when using nails or screws
punch – a hardened metal tool for cutting or marking

SUMMARY

■ Drills can be used for making holes or removing materials.
■ There are a range of different types. The smaller the drill the faster it must turn to prevent it breaking.
■ Punches are used for cutting holes or marking materials.

SUMMARY *activity*

In a piece of ply, drill a pattern of different sized holes using a range of drill bits. Glue different coloured wood into the holes and plane or sand flat.

44 Tools for holding materials

In this section of the book you will learn the following things:
- why you must use vices to hold materials when drilling;
- holding things firmly while sawing or cutting;
- clamping up while glues dry.

You will need to hold materials for a number of different reasons.

Clamping or holding for safety

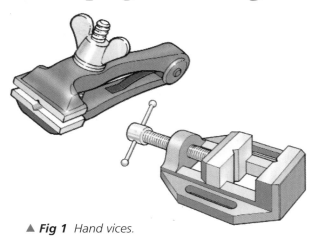

▲ *Fig 1* Hand vices.

When drilling materials with power or pillar drills, especially small pieces, you must not hold them with your fingers, even when drilling small holes. Often the drill will snatch the material from your fingers and may cut you badly. You can use a machine vice or a **hand vice** to hold the material (Fig 1).

Always support the material on a piece of wood to stop the drill snatching when it breaks through. When using a hand drill, this problem is not as great as you have more control over the drill. Place the small piece to be drilled on a sheet of glass paper to prevent it turning (Fig 2).

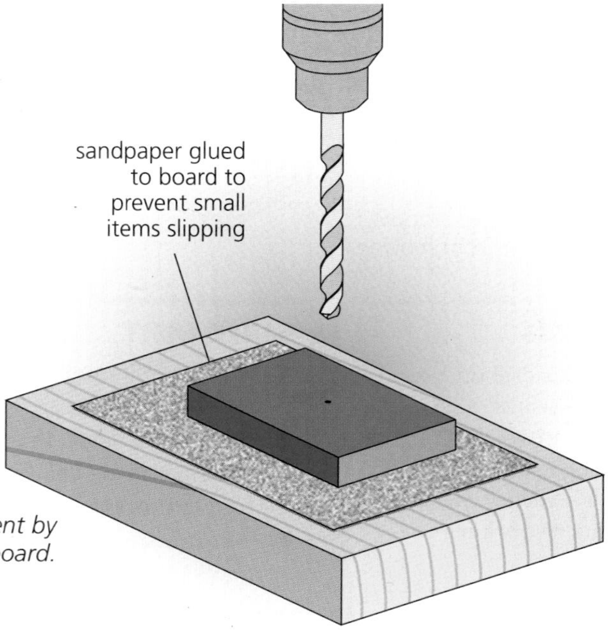

Q1 Why should you always hold small pieces in a vice when drilling?

sandpaper glued to board to prevent small items slipping

▶ *Fig 2* Preventing movement by drilling onto an abrasive board.

Clamping to hold firmly

When sawing, planing or screwing pieces together, you will need to use a vice. There are different types for wood and metal or plastics. Metal–working vices will need **soft jaws** to prevent marking polished metal or soft materials. Always saw carefully – the materials might break and cut your fingers. When sawing or drilling, try to keep the material low in the vice to prevent judder (Fig 3).

▲ **Fig 3** Working close to the vice.

Clamping until glue sets or solder cools

Glues can take hours to dry and the parts need to be pressed together. This can be done using G–clamps or, for longer materials, sash clamps. With large areas, you may need to clamp thicker blocks of wood to the surface to give even pressure all over the area. Sometimes you may have to make up **jigs** to hold odd shapes. These are blocks of wood cut to a shape which will hold the parts accurately (Fig 4).

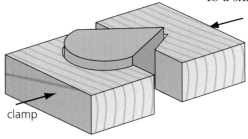

clamp

▲ **Fig 4** Using a jig.

When soldering or brazing, use metal clamps that can resist the temperature. In jewellery work, soft iron wire is used to tie things together; a little twist can take up expansion of the wire with heat (Fig 5).

Sometimes you can also use small split pins to hold pieces together.

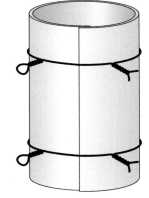

▶ **Fig 5** Using soft iron wire.

Q2 How do you stop the jaws of a vice from marking soft surfaces?

Q3 Why should metal clamps be used when soldering?

Key words

hand vice – a small hand-held vice

jig – a device to hold odd shaped work

soft jaws – they prevent work being marked

SUMMARY

■ You must hold work in a vice to prevent damage to your hands.

■ Clamping and holding can be used for several reasons: safety, holding still while gluing and holding while planing or sawing.

SUMMARY activity

Glue ten small pieces of veneer together. Clamp them together using two blocks of wood and a G-clamp and leave overnight to dry. File and cut to an attractive shape.

45 Tools for forming

In this section of the book you will learn the following things:
- how a vacuum forming machine works;
- how patterns are made;
- making domes using blow moulding.

Vacuum forming

Thermoplastics can be shaped by heating until they are soft and pulled over or pressed into a **pattern**. When they cool, they can be lifted from the pattern and trimmed to finish them.

Q1 Why are thermoplastics used in vacuum forming machines?

◄ *Fig 1* A vacuum forming machine.

In school you can use a vacuum forming machine (Fig 1). This has a platform which can be raised and lowered by a handle on the side of the machine. The pattern is put on this platform. The thermoplastic sheet is cut to size to suit your vacuum forming machine and its protective coating is removed. The thermoplastic sheet is then clamped into place, taking care to fit it exactly so that the vacuum can be formed with no leaks around the edges. The sheet should normally have its shiny side on top. The heater is pulled over the top of the plastic until it softens. When this happens, the heater is pushed back and the pattern lifted up. The vacuum is switched on and the air is sucked from under the plastic so it is pushed down onto the pattern. When it has cooled, the pattern can be lowered and the plastic removed from the machine (Fig 2).

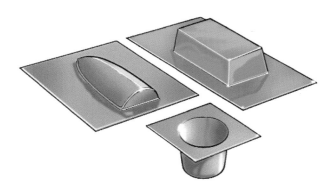

▲ *Fig 2* Example of vacuum forms.

The pattern must have sloping edges called the **draft**, so that the plastic can be removed easily from the pattern. If the pattern has a complicated shape, you may have to drill very small holes in it so that the vacuum can remove trapped air. All corners should be rounded (Fig 3).

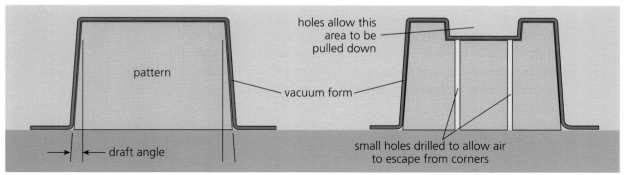

▲ **Fig 3** Draft angles and holes in patterns.

▲ **Fig 4** A blow-moulded buggy cover.

Q2 Why do patterns need a draft angle?

Q3 How can the pattern be altered to help certain parts pull down onto it?

Blow moulding

Blow moulding is similar to vacuum forming, but the thermoplastic is blown into a pattern. In school, some vacuum formers have attachments to blow domes. The plastic is held down by a ring and air is blown into the centre making the plastic form a dome. The air pressure must be kept high until the plastic has cooled, if not the dome will collapse (Fig 4).

Safety

When using the vacuum forming machine, do not leave it while it is heating as it could catch fire if the plastic sheet overheats.

Key words

draft – a sloping edge at an angle which helps the pattern to release from the vacuum form

pattern – an article from which a form is taken

thermoplastic – a plastic that can be heated and softened many times

SUMMARY

■ Vacuum and blow moulding relies on using thermoplastics. These soften when heated and harden when cool.

■ In a vacuum forming machine they are sucked down onto the pattern.

■ Blow moulding uses air pressure to blow the plastic into a mould or dome.

SUMMARY activity

Make a small pattern for vacuum forming a clown's face. You can use plaster or plasticine.

46 Systems

In this section of the book you will learn the following things:
- what a system is, and what it does;
- the parts of a system;
- how to find the system boundary.

We are surrounded by **systems**. Some are systems composed of people like schools, offices and factories and to do with the organisation of people. Others are like the railway systems, central heating systems, burglar alarms, or cookers.

Q1 Name a system found in your home.

▲ *Fig 1* An open loop system.

A system is a collection of connected things which perform a task. In Design and Technology, we use systems to explain how things work by breaking them down into simple boxes called **inputs**, **processes** and **outputs** (Fig 1). Sometimes another box is added called **feedback**. In a burglar alarm, the sensors on the doors and windows are the inputs. The process is the control box, and the outputs are the sirens and flashing lights. When a window is smashed or door forced, tiny electrical signals from the sensors are sent to the processor and are switched or amplified to make the siren sound and the lights flash. This is called an open loop system which is an on/off system.

When designing systems, all you need to consider are the boxes and what they do. For the burglar alarm input, a signal is produced when something changes, i.e. when the movement of the door is sensed. For the output, when a signal is produced then a light flashes. At this stage, you can design a system without knowing much about electronics. Some kits have the electronic components built into blocks and you just connect them together to do the job you want.

Sometimes, because finer control is needed, feedback is used in a closed loop system (Fig 2). This is taking some of the output and feeding back into the input. An example of feedback is when you are riding your bike and you want to turn a corner. You turn the handlebars. If you see that the bike is not turning enough, you turn them more. Your eyes are providing the feedback.

▲ **Fig 2** A closed loop system.

A system is sometimes made of subsystems joined together. You must decide which part you are studying and so define your own system boundary. In the burglar alarm (Fig 3), this will be only the sensors which protect the doors and windows, and the processor – not how the doors are fixed.

Input Door sensor

Input Window sensor

Input Panic button

Process

Output Siren Flashing light

◄ **Fig 3** A block diagram of a burglar alarm.

Q2 Can you think of another simple example of feedback?

Q3 What effect does feedback have?

Key words

feedback – taking some of the output back to the input

inputs – sensors, i.e. switches which produce an electrical output

outputs – devices which light up, sound or move when a voltage is applied

processes – amplifying or switching circuits

system – a collection of linked things

SUMMARY

■ Breaking a system down into parts can help you understand it better.

■ Systems enable you to use simple building blocks to make up more complex devices.

■ Feedback is used sometimes to control the system.

SUMMARY activity

Draw a block diagram of a system to warn someone in the house that it is raining and time to get in the washing.

47 Control

In this section of the book you will learn the following things:
- what control means;
- how control is used in school;
- the reasons why buffer boxes are used.

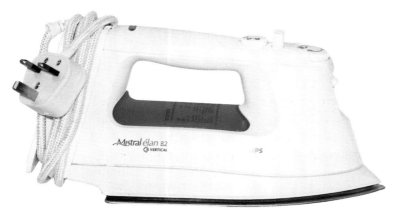

▲ **Fig 1** *Is there a control system in a steam iron?*

Q1 There is a control system in a steam iron – what is happening?

Inputs and outputs

When you ride your bicycle, you are using **control**. You are using the handlebars to steer (an input), and the pedals to move (another input). You see what effect the steering has by using your eyes and adjusting the handlebars (the feedback) to steer the right course (an output). In our homes, the central heating is a control system. When you grow, a biological control system is telling your body what to do.

Buffer boxes

In school, you can model control using a Smart box or **buffer box** connected to the computer. A control program running on the computer lets you tell it what you want it to do using a **control language**. This language is simple to use. You can type in phrases like *'Switchon1'* to switch on output 1. Similarly you can arrange for something to happen if an input is connected: *'If inputon1 then switchon1'*. Different languages have slightly different commands, so care is needed to use the correct ones for your programming. Some programs use **flowcharts** as a way of entering the commands.

▶ **Fig 2** *A maze-solving buggy.*

Projects, such as a buggy which can move around on its own, can use sensors to find the way out of a maze. When the buggy bumps into a wall, the sensor on that side makes contact and the computer program processes the information. It tells the outputs to switch the driving motors on or off or to reverse them to turn the buggy away from the wall (Fig 2).

Buffer boxes have eight inputs and eight outputs with LEDs to tell you whether the outputs are on or off. There is usually a switch to change the range of output voltages. It is then really easy to plug in the sensors and your motors to model a control system. Buffer boxes also prevent you damaging your computer when experimenting with control systems (Fig 3).

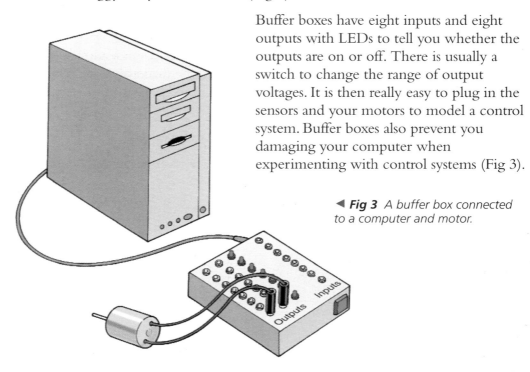

◄ **Fig 3** *A buffer box connected to a computer and motor.*

Q2 What does a control language allow you to do?

Q3 Why are buffer boxes used? Give two reasons.

Key words

buffer box – helps you connect inputs and outputs to a computer easily

control – using a computer to make a project work

control language – special commands to help you give instructions

flowchart – a logical list of instructions

SUMMARY

■ Computer control allows you to model systems using a buffer box. The box prevents you from damaging your computer.

■ A buffer box has connections for up to eight inputs and eight outputs. The outputs can be switched from five to 12 volts.

■ Computer control languages let you instruct the computer to process the information and act on it. Some use flowcharts to enter the commands.

SUMMARY ☞ *activity*

Write down the instructions to completely guide a blindfolded person around an obstacle such as a table, e.g. forward three steps, stop, turn left, stop, etc.

48 Input sensors

In this section of the book you will learn the following things:
- what input sensors do;
- how changes in light, movement, temperature and moisture can be sensed;
- the uses of the different sensors to control things.

Sensing changes

Input **sensors** usually convert a change in light, movement, temperature or humidity into changes in electrical signals. A simple sensor can be made of copper foil which is glued across a window. If the window is broken, the foil breaks and the current is switched off.

There are many different types of **switches** which can be used as **on/off** sensors:

Microswitches have a very light action and can have levers attached so something touching them lightly will make them switch.

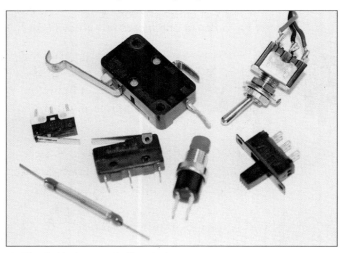

▲ *Fig 1* *Various on/off switches.*

Tilt switches have a little ball of mercury which can short out two contacts when tilted. You can make your own tilt switches using a ball of foil in a plastic film can with pieces of thick wire pushed through the bottom to make the contacts.

Magnetic switches are switches which are operated by a magnet. The magnet does not touch the switch but passes close by. They are used in burglar alarms. The magnet is put in a hole drilled in a door and the switch is drilled into the door jamb. When the magnet moves, the switch operates (Fig 1).

Pressure switches are usually put under the mats in shops to tell the shopkeeper when someone enters – they make contact when stepped on (Fig 2).

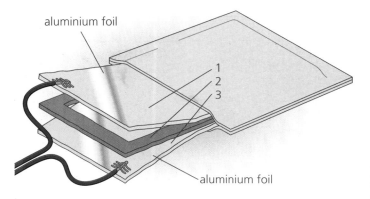

aluminium foil

1
2
3

aluminium foil

▲ *Fig 2* *Pressure switches.*

Q1 How could a pressure switch be used in a museum or jewellery shop?

There are three other types of components which will sense light, temperature and moisture:

Photoresistors change their resistance with light. When the light falling on one increases, its resistance decreases. This can be used to vary a voltage and switch equipment when the light changes.

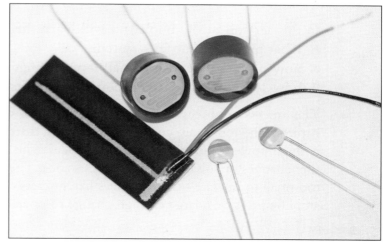

▲ *Fig 3* *Photoresistors and thermistors.*

Thermistors are similar to photoresistors, except that their resistance changes with temperature (Fig 3).

▲ *Fig 4* *A PCB moisture detector.*

Moisture sensors have two grids of wires. When water falls on the grids, the sensor's resistance falls. These usually have to be homemade using a **PCB** (Fig 4).

Sensors have two connections which are connected to circuits or a computer Smart Box to control other devices.

Q2 A device is needed to warn an old person that their bath water is too hot. What sensor would you use?

Q3 Where could you use a moisture sensor?

Key words

on/off switch – switch with only two states called on or off sometimes shown as 1 or 0

PCB – a printed circuit board

sensors – devices that can sense temperature, heat, light and moisture

switch – breaks an electrical circuit when a button, lever or toggle is operated

SUMMARY

- Sensors detect changes in physical properties such as movement, light, temperature and convert them into changes in voltage or current.
- Switches are on/off devices; other sensors like photoresistors change their values gradually.
- There are many uses for sensors in alarms and heating control of buildings.

SUMMARY *activity*

Make a small card box, with a lid. Use aluminium baking foil and paper clips to make a switch which operates when the lid is opened.

49 Processes

In this section of the book you will learn the following things:
- what processors do in a system;
- how processors convert small input changes into usable outputs;
- how several inputs can be compared to each other.

The process or processor is the part of a control system which reacts to the **inputs**. The inputs are combined, switched, **timed** or **amplified** to provide enough power to drive the **output** devices. The inputs of a system are often tiny changes of voltage, current or resistance. These changes on their own are too small to operate output devices like buzzers or motors, so they have to be amplified to give a large enough change to operate the output devices.

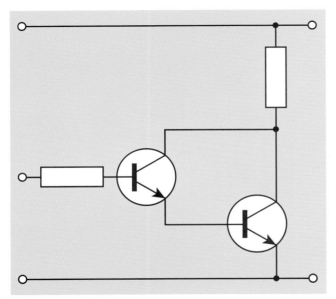

▲ **Fig 1** A Darlington Pair high gain amplifier circuit.

Q1 What is the main purpose of the process in a system?

Sometimes the output needs just to be switched on or off. This could be achieved using a switching circuit. Often these circuits are high **gain** amplifiers which flip from off to on very quickly (Fig 1). In tape or video players, the input is a small signal which has to be amplified into a larger output. This larger output signal will then drive the speakers or earphones. The more accurate the copy, the better it sounds or looks to you (Fig 2).

CD player
very small
signal input

▶ **Fig 2** An amplifier amplifying a small signal into a larger one.

Amplifier

Headphones
larger amplified
signal

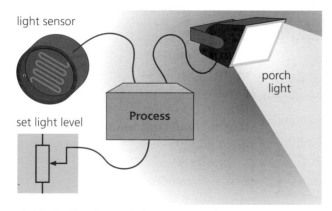

light sensor

porch light

set light level

Process

▲ **Fig 3** *Two inputs being compared.*

Sometimes, two or more inputs have to be compared with each other. When the right conditions are met, the processor produces an output. Imagine a porch light which comes on as it gets dark. A light dependent resistor changes its value as darkness falls. The circuit compares this with a value from an adjustable resistor which lets you set the level at which the light comes on. When the level is reached, the circuit switches on the porch light (Fig 3).

When you open a car door at night, the courtesy light comes on and usually stays on for a time until the driver has started the car. In this case, a sensor in the door (a switch) starts a timer (the process) running which keeps the light on for a time and then switches it off (Fig 4).

Q2 In cassette or video players, why is it essential that an accurate copy of the input is produced?

Q3 How does a light dependent resistor change when light falls on it?

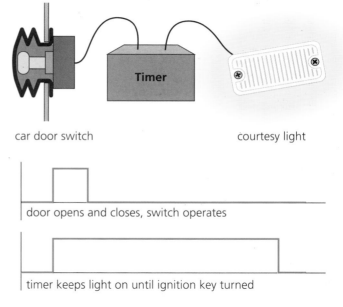

car door switch

Timer

courtesy light

door opens and closes, switch operates

timer keeps light on until ignition key turned

▲ **Fig 4** *A timer circuit.*

Key words

amplifier – a circuit which makes small signals larger

gain – how many times an amplifier multiplies the input signal

input – a signal which controls a circuit

output – the signal which controls the motors and buzzers, etc

timer – a circuit which stays on or off for a time after receiving an input signal

SUMMARY

- Inputs often produce very small changes of voltage, current or resistance.
- Processors combine, time or amplify these changes into big enough signals to operate the output devices.
- Some processors switch on or off; others produce accurate amplification of the input signals.

SUMMARY activity

Draw a block diagram of a system so that it will let you know if someone enters your bedroom. You must use two different input sensors.

50 Output devices

In this section of the book you will learn the following things:
- what output devices are;
- what they are used for;
- how electrical signals can produce changes in sound, light and movement.

Output devices are those which convert electrical signals into sound, light or movement. Some are used to tell us that something is happening – they are indicators. Others can make parts of your project move.

Producing sound

Speakers are used in radios and audio equipment and need an alternating current to make sound.

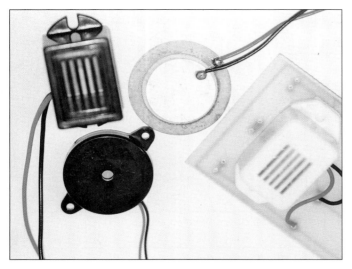

Sirens are the devices which make the high-pitched and very loud noises in burglar or personal alarms. Some need an alternating current to make a sound, whilst others just require a direct current.

Buzzers and bells make a noise and they need a DC voltage to work (Fig 1).

Q1 When would you use a buzzer in a child's game project?

◀ **Fig 1** Some buzzers and sounders.

Producing movement

Electric motors convert an electrical current into rotary movement, so can be used to drive the wheels of buggies or other moving parts in your projects (Fig 2).

Solenoids provide a push or pull movement which can operate a lever or push open a door on a model.

▶ **Fig 2** Different sizes of electric motors.

Linear actuators are electric motors with a gearbox which drives a shaft in and out. They are used for precise straight line, or linear, movement. **Actuators** are more controllable than solenoids (Fig 3).

Q2 Where could you use a linear actuator on a toy dumper truck or bulldozer?

▲ *Fig 3* A linear actuator.

Producing light

Lamps, sometimes called bulbs, convert electricity into light and some heat. There are lots of different types. Inside the glass bulb is a wire filament which glows white hot when a current passes through it.

Light emitting diodes (LED) are solid state lamps, usually only bright enough to use as indicators. They take much less current than lamps and are smaller. They need a series resistor and must be fitted the correct way round. They are available in a range of colours and sizes (Fig 4).

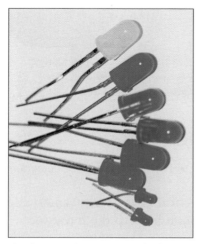

▲ *Fig 4* Light emitting diodes.

Q3 Give two reasons for using LEDs instead of lamps in a project.

Operating switches

Relays are a type of solenoid. When the coil has a current passed through it, the solenoid moves electrical contacts. These contacts can then be used to control higher currents and voltages.

All of these devices have two leads, and can be connected to the output sockets of a **Smart or buffer box**.

Key words

actuator – a device which operates something

relay – a solenoid operated switch

Smart or buffer box – a box connected to a computer, which enables you to plug in inputs and output devices easily

SUMMARY

■ Output devices produce sound, light, or movement when connected to a voltage or signal.

■ They can be used as warning indicators or to make projects move.

SUMMARY activity

Design a card dinosaur or space creature which uses two yellow LEDs as eyes.

51 Feedback

In this section of the book you will learn the following things:
- what feedback is;
- how feedback is used in real situations;
- what stability and lag is.

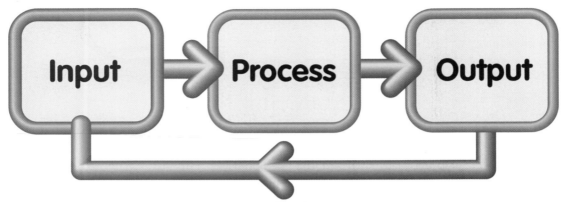

Feedback
taking some of the output and using it to modify the input

▲ *Fig 1 A system block diagram.*

Better control

Feedback can be found in all types of systems from production lines to mechanical and electronic systems. It is taking part of the output and feeding it back to the input to improve the control and to get a more responsive system. It also makes external influences have less effect on the system (Fig 1).

Q1 Give one reason why feedback is used.

Imagine a shower where the controls are hot and cold water taps. When you start to adjust them, the water is the right temperature but when it comes out of the shower head, it feels too hot. You increase the cold and decrease the hot and the water then starts to get too cold. Although there is feedback in the system, i.e. your body sensing the temperature of the water and you turning it down, there is a **lag** between control and output. A better shower design would control the water temperature more sensitively and the system would have **stability**. Stability happens when a system tries to resist change (Fig 2).

◀ *Fig 2 A shower system.*

Feedback; is it too hot or cold?

How may produced?

▲ *Fig 3* *A bakery system with feedback.*

If, in a large bakery, the stock of bread and cakes was increasing, then the stock control person could tell the bakers to slow down. The nearer they were to having the stockrooms full, the less the bakers would have to make. In this case the input, the 'making', is controlled by the output, the stock in store. The stock control person is 'doing' the feedback. If the stock controller was slow in reporting how full the storeroom was, then this would introduce a lag in the system. There then might be times when the storeroom was full and no more could be stored, or times when the storeroom might be nearly empty (Fig 3).

In electronic systems, it is easier to see the effects of feedback – the system may not be as complicated as those involving people. In central heating systems, a sensor feeds back the temperature of the room to the controller on the boiler and switches it on or off to maintain the correct room temperature. Systems without feedback are called **open loop**; systems with feedback are called **closed loop**.

> **Q2** In the bakery example, what reason could there be for a full storeroom?
>
> **Q3** Why is a system with feedback called a closed loop system?

Key words

closed loop – a system with feedback

feedback – control of the input of a system by referring to the output

lag – the time it takes a system to respond to change

open loop – a system without feedback

stability – the resistance to change in a system

SUMMARY

- Feedback is a method of controlling systems, whether mechanical, electronic or biological.
- It is comparing the output with the input to make a more accurate system.
- Systems with stability resist changes and try to quickly return to their original states.
- Lag is how long it takes for a system to react to change.

SUMMARY activity

Draw a block diagram of the bakery system above.

52 Mechanisms

In this section of the book you will learn the following things:
- what mechanisms are;
- what mechanisms do;
- how rotary and linear motion is achieved.

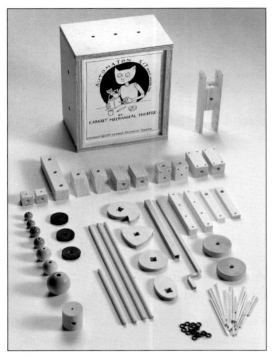

▲ **Fig 1** A group of mechanisms.

Changing movement

A mechanism is a system which converts one sort of movement into another. It usually contains levers, cams, gears or pulleys (Fig 1). It can be just one lever or cam or, for example, a whole group of linked **components**. A mechanism can convert a **rotary** motion into a **linear** motion or vice versa. On a sewing machine, an electric motor drives a mechanism made up of pulleys, gears and levers, changing a rotary motion into a linear motion. The linear motion is the needle being moved up and down. An electric food mixer converts the rotary motion of an electric motor into the rotary motion of the beaters. These can be slowed down or speeded up by the use of gears or pulleys. The motor may be at right angles to the beaters so the mechanism changes the direction of the motion as well.

Machines are groups of mechanisms and structures which do useful work. If you think of a car, it is a vast collection of all types of mechanisms connected to a rigid structure, the body. All of these mechanisms make something happen, whether it is to turn the car around, reverse it or stop it. The pedals are levers; the gearbox contains gears. The engine has pulleys to drive various parts like the water pump.

▶ **Fig 2** A mechanism in a toy.

Most mechanisms are hidden away inside equipment – sometimes the best places to see them are on old machinery such as clocks, traction engines, steam trains and farm machinery (Fig 3). Some educational toys show their brightly coloured mechanisms so that youngsters can be entertained by the movement. These are often useful if you are unsure how a mechanism works or what it does. There are also kits such as Fischer Technik or Lego Dacta which let you build mechanisms easily (Fig 4). Making your own mechanisms can involve measuring out and drilling very accurately so that gears and pulleys run very freely. **Friction** will cause power to be wasted.

▲ **Fig 3** A traction engine.

◄ **Fig 4** A kit gear box.

Q1 What mechanism will you find on a bicycle?

Q2 What type of motion does a food mixer produce?

Q3 What two mechanisms are used in grandfather clocks?

Key words

component – a part of a mechanism

friction – occurs when two surfaces rub against each other

linear – a straight line

machine – a device which does work using moving and fixed components

rotary – turning

SUMMARY

■ Mechanisms convert one type of motion into another type.

■ They can be composed of a single mechanism or a group of mechanisms linked together.

■ Mechanisms are generally hidden from our view inside equipment such as video recorders and electric tools.

SUMMARY activity

Take three different machines used in your home and draw an outline of them. Write down which mechanisms you think they contain.

53 Levers

In this section of the book you will learn the following things:

- what levers are;
- the three different orders of levers;
- how levers are used in everyday objects.

A lever is a rigid bar or rod which pivots at a single point called the **fulcrum**. The input force is called the **effort** and the output force, the **load**. If you use a screwdriver to open a tin of paint, then you are using a lever. If you are using a joystick with your computer, then the handle is a lever which converts the large movements of your hand into smaller ones to operate the electronics inside the base of the stick (Fig 1). Levers are used to move things and give mechanical advantage. There are three classes or orders of lever, based on where the load and effort are applied and where the fulcrum is in relation to both.

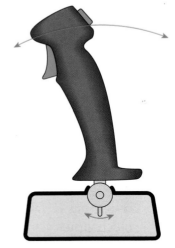
▲ **Fig 1** Cross-section of a joystick.

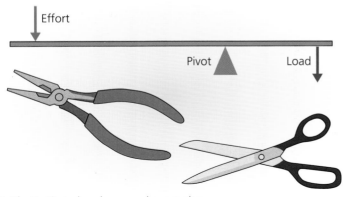
▲ **Fig 2** First-class lever and examples.

First-class levers

First-class (or order) levers have the fulcrum between the load and the effort. Examples are scissors, pliers, computer joysticks and crowbars. The amount of **mechanical advantage** depends on the position of the fulcrum in relation to the load and effort (Fig 2).

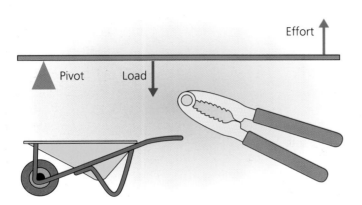
▲ **Fig 3** Second-class lever and examples.

Second-class levers

Second-class (or order) levers have the fulcrum at one end of the lever and the effort is applied at the other. The load is somewhere in between. Examples are a wheelbarrow and nutcrackers (Fig 3).

Third-class levers

Third-class (or order) levers have the fulcrum at one end and the load at the other end. The effort is somewhere in between. Examples are tweezers, chopsticks and a fishing rod (Fig 4).

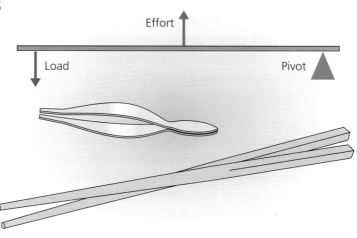

▲ **Fig 4** *Third-class lever and examples.*

All levers give **mechanical advantage**, either in distance moved or reduction of effort.

$$\text{Mechanical advantage} \ = \ \frac{\text{load}}{\text{effort}} \ = \ \frac{x}{y}$$

Velocity ratio is the distance moved by the effort compared to the distance moved by the body

$$\text{Velocity ratio} \ = \ \frac{\text{distance moved by effort}}{\text{distance moved by load}}$$

Q1 Why do scissors cut better near the fulcrum than at the tip?

Q2 Where is the fulcrum on a pair of nutcrackers?

Q3 What order of lever is a car park barrier?

Key words

effort – the force put into a system
fulcrum – a pivot point
load – the force exerted on a structure
mechanical advantage – how much the effort is amplified
velocity ratio – a comparison of the distances moved by the effort and the load

SUMMARY

- There are three orders of lever: first, second and third, depending on where the fulcrum is compared to the load and effort.
- Levers can be used to convert large movements into small ones.
- Small forces can be converted into large ones but as energy cannot be created or destroyed, then the distances travelled by the load and the effort must be different.

SUMMARY activity

Cut a strip of thick card 200 mm long, draw a centre line and punch small holes every 10 mm. Use a drawing pin as a fulcrum and pin through the centre hole to a board. Move one end up 50 mm and check to see how far the other end moves. Repeat for each hole. What happens?

54 Cams

In this section of the book you will learn the following things:
- that cams convert rotary motion to linear motion;
- cams can have different shapes to provide a range of movement;
- followers are used to transmit movement freely.

Cams are wheels with either an off-centre **axis** or they have an irregular shape. They are used where a rotary motion needs to be converted into a linear one. Usually a device called a **follower** is used, to follow the shape of the outside edge of the cam which will make it go up and down (Fig 1). Washing machine controllers are motor driven cams which turn slowly and operate microswitches – these switch the water and soap in the machine on and off.

Q1 What is the simplest way to make a cam?

An **eccentric cam** is a circle of material which has its axis not central. When it is rotated, the outside edge will move up and down by the amount of the offset. If a follower is rested on the cam, it moves in a wave-like motion (Fig 2). The mechanism could be used to make a model boat or waves move in a project.

▲ **Fig 1** A cam operated toy.

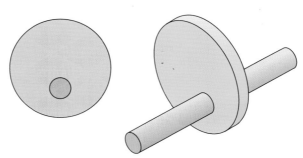

▲ **Fig 2** An eccentric cam.

A pear-shaped cam has one half which is a true circle but the other half is elongated so, for half the rotation, the follower will not move, but for the other half, the follower will rise and fall (Fig 3).

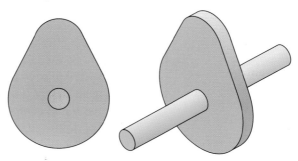

▲ **Fig 3** A pear-shaped cam.

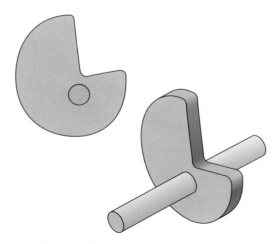

A **snail cam** has a step in its outside edge and can only be rotated in one direction. The follower will slowly rise and then suddenly fall back (Fig 4). You could use this cam to operate a toy crocodile's mouth. It would open slowly and snap shut.

Q2 Why will snail cams only rotate in one direction?

▲ *Fig 4* *A snail cam.*

Followers can just rub on the edge of a cam, but often friction will make it stiff to turn. Sometimes, the follower will have a roller on the end to reduce the friction and to make it more free running. Some can have a disc which will turn as well as rise and fall (Fig 5). Followers must slide very freely to operate easily. You can make a lever rest on the cam and overlap the cam – this could operate a puppet's strings.

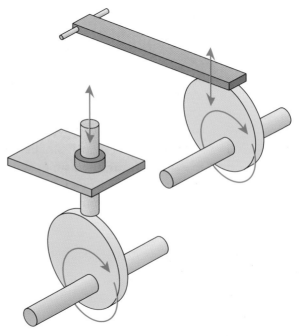

▶ *Fig 5* *Different types of follower.*

Q3 How can you make followers operate smoothly?

Key words

axis – the centre of rotation
eccentric cam – a circular cam with offset axis
follower – a slider which rubs on the outside edge of a cam
snail cam – a snail-shaped cam

SUMMARY

■ Cams are wheels with irregular shape.
■ They convert rotary movement to linear movement.
■ They are used as controllers for washing machines and can be used in toys.
■ A follower usually rubs on the edge of the cam and so slides up and down.

SUMMARY activity

Use a smooth plastic lid from a food container. Cut a disc of polystyrene foam and glue on the inside. Drill an off-centre hole and fix a piece of dowel as an axle. Mount the axle through holes in a cardboard box. Use your cam to make the moving part of a sign.

55 Gears

In this section of the book you will learn the following things:
- what gears are used for;
- the different types of gears;
- how to calculate gear ratios.

Spur gears are wheels which have teeth cut or moulded into their edge – these **mesh** with other gears and transmit rotary motion. They are usually made of metal or plastic but wooden ones can be found in windmills and very old clocks. If two gears mesh, they rotate in opposite directions. If you want both gears turning in the same direction, put an **idler gear** between the two main gears. This will not affect the ratio.

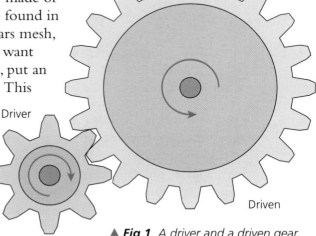

▲ **Fig 1** A driver and a driven gear.

Gears are either driver or driven gears. If an electric motor has a small gear on its shaft, then this is called the driver gear and the gear that this one meshes with is the driven gear (Fig 1). If the driver gear is smaller than the driven gear, then there will be a reduction in the speed of rotation. The **gear ratio** is the distance moved by the output or the number of teeth on the output gear compared to the distance moved by the input or the number of teeth on the input gear.

$$\text{Gear ratio} \quad = \quad \frac{\text{number of teeth on driven gear}}{\text{number of teeth on driver gear}}$$

Q1 How can you work out the ratio of a pair of gears?

Q2 If you have a driver gear with 10 teeth and a driven gear of 100 teeth, what is the ratio?

Gears can be linked together if high gear ratios are needed. Linked gears are called gear trains or compound gears. Gear trains are used in vehicles to transmit power from the engine to the wheels and are known as gearboxes (Fig 2).

▲ **Fig 2** A gear train.

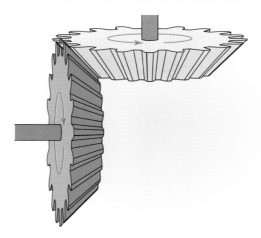

▲ **Fig 3** Bevel gears.

Rack and pinion gears are used where rotary motion needs to be changed to linear motion. They have a straight toothed strip which meshes with a gear. A common use is in mountain railways, where the rack is between the track, and the **pinion** gear is on the train (Fig 4).

Worm gears are used where a drive is needed at 90° to the original direction. It has the advantage that drive can only go from the worm wheel through the worm gear and *not* in the other direction. They are often used in cranes where the load should not drive back through the gear train (Fig 5).

When making gear trains, you will have to be very accurate when measuring and drilling holes so that the gears run freely.

The teeth of bevel gears are cut at an angle of 45°, so that when two gears mesh together they are at 90°, allowing the direction of drive to be changed (Fig 3).

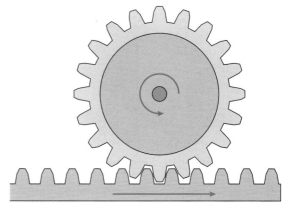

▲ **Fig 4** Rack and pinion.

▲ **Fig 5** Worm gear.

Q3 Why is a worm gear especially useful?

Key words

gear ratio – a comparison of the number of teeth on the output and input gears

idler gear – a small gear fitted in between two gears so that they turn in the same direction

mesh – link together

pinion – a smaller gear

SUMMARY

■ Gears are toothed wheels which mesh with each other. They transmit rotary motion.

■ There are driver and driven gears, which rotate in opposite directions. An idler wheel can be fitted to make two gears rotate in the same direction.

SUMMARY activity

Use a gears kit such as Fischer Technik or Lego Technic to make up a gear train with a ratio of 100 :1.

56 Pulleys

In this section of the book you will learn the following things:
- why pulleys are used;
- how velocity ratios are calculated;
- how to use pulleys in school projects.

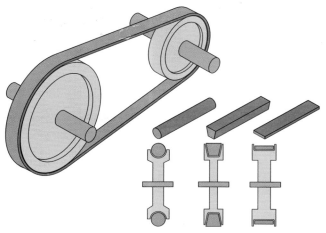

▲ **Fig 1** *Pulley sections showing round, vee and flat.*

Pulleys are grooved wheels on which **drive belts** run. Drive belts can be **flat**, vee or **round** in section, designed to run in a groove (Fig 1). They transmit rotary action by relying on friction. They are very quiet and are used to prevent vibration and noise being transmitted to other parts of the mechanism. They are used in tumble driers and washing machines for this reason. They are also cheap to produce compared with gears. Unlike gears, pulleys always rotate in the same direction unless a twisted belt is used (Fig 2).

They are good to use in school projects as there is less need for accurate assembly and slight inaccuracies are taken up by the belt. Belts can be made from strong elastic bands or sections cut from cycle inner tubes.

Q1 What is an advantage of using a pulley?

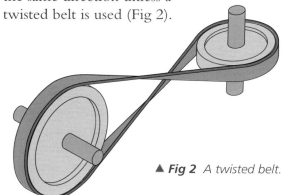

▲ **Fig 2** *A twisted belt.*

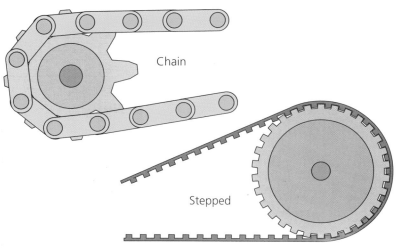

Chain

Stepped

▲ **Fig 3** *Chain drive and stepped belt.*

The shapes of **V and A belts** provide a larger surface area to grip the pulley, but for high loads **stepped belts** or chain drives are often used (Fig 3). Stepped belts ensure that the pulleys do not slip relative to each other and are more like gears than pulley systems. These are used in car engines, computer printers and plotters. An example of a chain drive is on a bicycle.

When making a model buggy for a project, fix the motor and then use a strong elastic band around its **shaft** and the wheel. The shaft is much smaller than the wheel and so reduces the speed of the wheel, making the buggy move at a sensible speed (Fig 4). The small diameter pulley may have to turn many times to make the larger pulley turn once. Small motors turn extremely quickly and

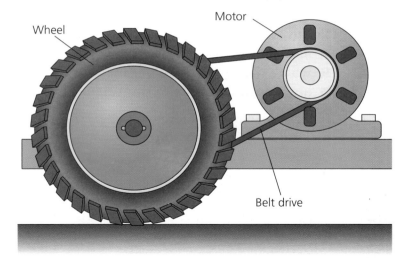

▲ *Fig 4* Motor drive on a buggy.

always have to be used with gears or pulleys. The velocity ratio is usually given as two numbers e.g. 100:1. This means that the driver pulley will have to turn 100 times to make the driven pulley turn once.

$$\text{Velocity ratio} = \frac{\text{diameter of driven pulley}}{\text{diameter of driver pulley}}$$

Q2 Why are belts differently shaped?

Q3 Why are chain drives sometimes used instead of pulleys?

Key words

drive belts – soft rubber or plastic materials used with pulleys.

pulley – a wheel with a groove in its rim for a belt to run in

shaft – the output of an electric motor.

stepped, flat, round, V and A belts – different belt sections

SUMMARY

- Pulleys are wheels with various shaped grooves in their rims in which drive belts run.
- They transmit rotary motion.
- They run very quietly.
- Both pulleys turn in the same direction, however, twisting the belt can reverse this.
- They are easy to use for school projects as you do not have to be very accurate aligning the pulleys.

SUMMARY activity

Make two pulleys of different sizes from cardboard discs; use an elastic band as a belt. Work out the velocity ratio for your pulleys.

57 Changing types of movement

In this section of the book you will learn the following things:
- mechanisms which convert one type of movement into another;
- where the mechanisms are used;
- how to make examples from simple materials.

Linear movement is movement in a straight line, i.e. backwards and forwards. It is sometimes called reciprocating movement.

Rotary movement is circular movement. In mechanisms, we often want one type of movement converted to the other. While cams and followers are the usual method, there are other mechanisms which can be used.

Q1 What is linear movement?

Rack and pinions are usually made from metal gears, but they can be made in school from **MDF** and **dowel** using accurate drilling (Fig 1).

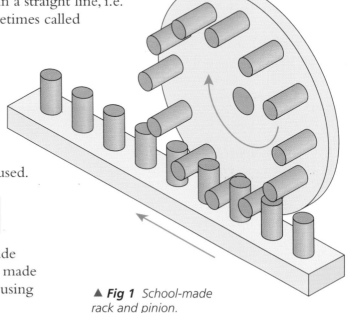

▲ *Fig 1* *School-made rack and pinion.*

Crank and sliders have one part sliding in a tube or between guides. This is pushed backwards and forwards by a connecting rod driven by a rotating disc or crank. The most common uses are in petrol engines where the crankshaft rotates and pushes the piston up and down using a connecting rod (Fig 2). You can make a simple crank by putting two right angle bends in metal or plastic rods. The amount of slider movement depends on the distance between the two bends and is called the **throw**.

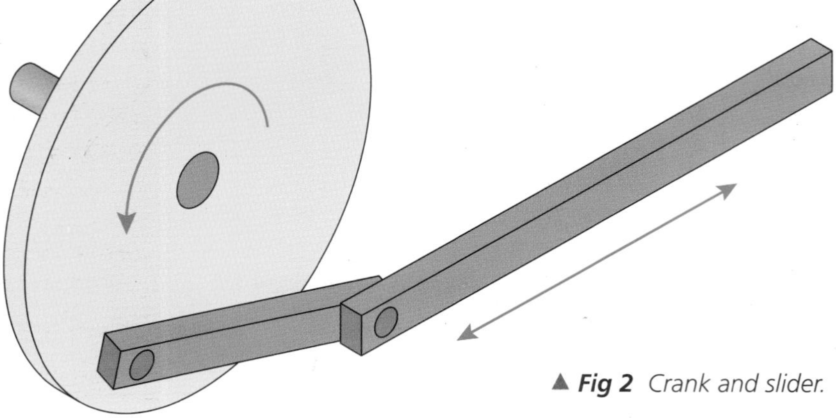

▲ *Fig 2* *Crank and slider.*

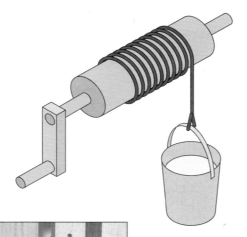

A weight on a string which is wrapped around a **shaft** will provide rotary movement from a linear pull. This will cause the shaft to turn, and is used to power some old clocks. Used in the other direction, turning the handle of a well will lift the bucket – a linear movement. This mechanism is called a windlass (Fig 3).

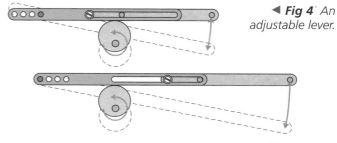

◀ *Fig 4* An adjustable lever.

▲ *Fig 3*
A windlass.

A cam and lever together can give an adjustable linear movement. You can adjust the pivot point and length of the lever to provide just the right amount of movement (Fig 4).

Cam **followers** can be disc shaped, so that when the cam turns, the follower will turn and go up and down. It will turn randomly depending upon the friction between the cam and follower (Fig 5).

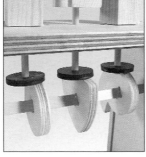

▲ *Fig 5* *Rotary and linear movement.*

Linear actuators use an electric motor to turn a threaded nut which then drives a threaded rod in or out. The rod will move backwards or forwards slowly reducing the fast motor speed, the rod and the nut acting as a gear reduction (Fig 6).

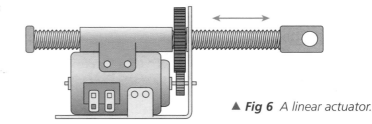

▲ *Fig 6* *A linear actuator.*

Q2 How do the weights on a grandfather clock make it work?

Q3 What is a common use for a crank mechanism?

Key words

dowel – round piece of wood used for joining materials
follower – a slider which rubs on the outside edge of a cam
MDF – medium density fibreboard
shaft – the rod on which a gear, pulley or cam rotates
throw – the movement a crank gives

SUMMARY

- We often need to change the direction of movement.
- Linear to rotary movement is used in many machines. Examples include car engines, clocks and steam engines.

SUMMARY *activity*

Use thin plastic sheet or a construction kit to make a model of a crank and slider as in Fig 2.

58 Linking mechanisms

In this section of the book you will learn the following things:
- how to use different mechanisms together;
- how to make noises with mechanisms;
- changing the direction of movement.

Changing movement

Mechanisms are often used together to produce different or more complicated movement. Sometimes you can use lots of gears in a gearbox or many pulleys or cams working together, but often several different types of mechanisms can be joined together to give different movements. This can usually be seen best in **automata**.

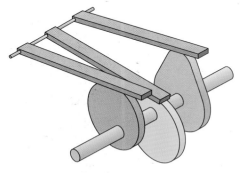

▲ **Fig 1** *Cams and levers.*

Q1 What are the advantages of using combinations of mechanisms?

The simplest combination is using a **lever** resting on a **cam**. This produces an up and down movement which can be altered by repositioning the fulcrum. The shape of the cam is important as it will change the sort of movement at the end of the lever (Fig 1).

If the cam has flat surfaces and the lever is made of springy wood fixed at one end, when the cam is turned the lever will bend up, and then snap down making a loud noise. This can be increased if the end of the lever can hit a fixed block of wood (Fig 2). Some cams are cut with very coarse teeth to make a higher pitched noise which can be useful for toys.

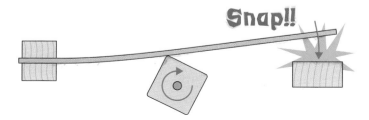

▲ **Fig 2** *Noises!*

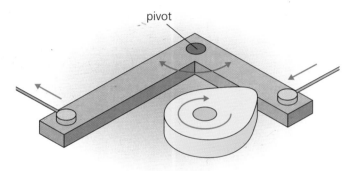

▲ **Fig 3** *A bellcrank.*

Bellcranks change the direction of a motion, usually through 90°. They were used to operate the bells in old houses using cords or wires which went under the floorboards, giving them the name. They are really a lever with a bend where the pivot is. They can be used really well with cams. Increasing the length of the arm increases the amount of travel (Fig 3).

Gears and levers are often used in cranes to raise the arm of the crane. The chain hook can be raised by turning a handle operating a windlass (Fig 4).

▶ *Fig 4* *An old crane.*

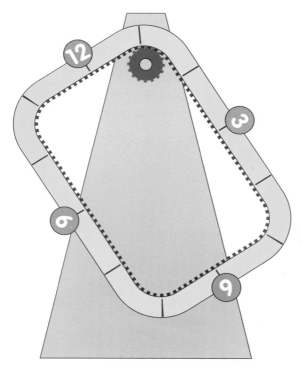

▲ *Fig 5* *A novel clock using sun and planet gears.*

Most gears have the teeth on the outside edge of the gear, but there are gears which have the teeth on an inside edge. These are called sun and planet gears, because they move like the planets around the sun. This modern clock makes use of this type of gear (Fig 5).

Q2 In what type of toy could the noise-making mechanism be used?

Q3 What advantages are there in using gears?

Key words

automata – model figures which move when handles are turned

bellcrank – a lever with an angle at the fulcrum

cam – a shaped disc or eccentric wheel

lever – a rod pivoted along its length

SUMMARY

- More complicated movements can be made by using a combination of mechanisms.
- Gears, levers and pulleys are often used in cranes.
- Some mechanisms can make noises as they turn.

SUMMARY activity

Make a model of a bellcrank and a cam using polystyrene modelling foam.

59 Recognising structures

In this section of the book you will learn the following things:
- how to recognise different types of structures;
- what structures do;
- how to make and model structures.

We are surrounded by **structures**. Some occur naturally like those in plants, the feathers of birds or even our skeletons. Some are made by us, e.g. buildings, electricity pylons and bridges. Structures all have some common elements: they can carry the **load** for which they were designed and they support the parts of the object in the correct position (Fig 1).

◄ **Fig 1** *Various structures.*

> **Q1** What are the two basic types of structures?

For example, your skeleton supports your muscles and soft tissues in the correct positions and allows them to work. The bones in your legs are strong enough to take the forces of your running, jumping and standing still without breaking or bending too much. The parts of a bridge do the same job. It stays in place, despite the loads such as vehicles and people which we put on it. Some structures, such as the bones and feathers of birds, do a successful job despite having to be very light themselves. In aircraft the same principle applies – we use new

▲ **Fig 2** *A framed structure.*

composite materials which are really strong but are very light. In the case of buildings and bridges, weight is not as important, but the more materials used the more costly the structures become.

Types of structure

There are several types of structures. **Mass structures** like dams and retaining walls use their weight to support things. **Framed structures** like bridges have lots of interlinked struts or bars (Fig 2). **Shell structures** are made of sheet material, and include car bodies, petrol tanker containers and ships (Fig 3). Bridges can be beams supported at both ends, or they can be cantilevered in which case they are supported only at one end just like a crane.

Model structures can be built from plastic drinking straws or spaghetti (uncooked!). Glue them together using a glue gun (Fig 4). There are kits available in which the components are just clipped together. Some kits even have small measuring devices which can be fitted to let you see the loads at different places.

▲ *Fig 3* A shell structure.

▼ *Fig 4* A spaghetti bridge.

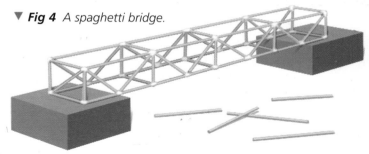

Q2 What type of structure is a ship's hull?

Q3 What type of structure is the Eiffel Tower in Paris?

Key words

composite material – a material made up of several others
framed structure – a framework of parts
load – force applied to a structure
mass structure – a structure which resists forces with its own weight
shell structure – a structure made of sheet materials
structure – a body which resists forces without changing shape too much

SUMMARY

- There are naturally occurring structures all around us: plants, trees and skeletons. Buildings, bridges and pylons are examples of made structures.
- All structures support loads in their correct places.
- Using new composite materials, we can make very strong yet lightweight structures.
- There are three basic types of structure: mass, framed and shell.

SUMMARY activity

Use ten drinking straws and a glue gun to make the highest structure you can, to support a £1 coin.

60 Compression

In this section of the book you will learn the following things:
- what compression forces are;
- how compression forces affect materials;
- how materials are chosen to resist compression forces.

Structures are subjected to many different types of **load**. If a force is put on a part or **member** of a structure which attempts to squash it, then this force is called compression (Fig 1).

Q1 What is a common word for compression?

If you made a tall column of modelling clay and either pushed down on it or put a weight on it, it would squash down, probably swelling out at the sides. This would show that clay was poor in compression. If you then tried the same experiment with a block of wood, it would take a great deal of force to reduce the length of the wood, but at some stage it would eventually break or fail. This would show that wood was excellent in compression (Fig 2). Coalminers used wooden pit props to hold up the roofs of coal mines. However, resistance to compression also depends on the dimensions of the material – a thin bamboo cane will bend and snap when compressive forces are applied.

▲ **Fig 1** Compression forces.

Q2 If you put a compression force on a bamboo cane, why would it break?

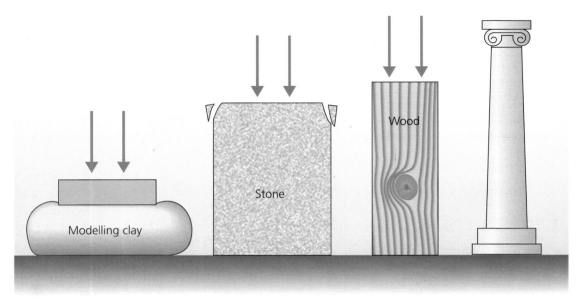

▲ **Fig 2** Modelling clay, stone and wood in compression.

Static and dynamic loads

When you are standing, the bones in your spine and legs are in compression. Bones are also good in compression. When you are standing still, you have **static** loads acting on your bones, but if you start to run, then the loads will change all the time. These are said to be **dynamic** loads. Materials are chosen to withstand the loads which are likely to be put on them. If the designer knows that compressive loads are needed, then he or she will choose a material like steel, stone or wood to deal with these forces. If the calculations and choice are faulty, then the structure will fail. Structures will have all types of loads acting on them so the choice of materials may not be a simple one. Some of the compression loads of structures are due to their own weight and this may be the largest of all of the loads on the structure (Fig 3).

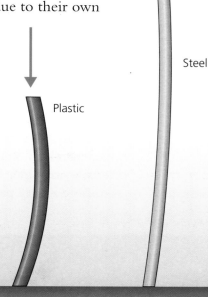

Steel

Plastic

Wood

▲ *Fig 3* Dimensions make a difference.

Q3 What type of force is acting on the legs of a table?

Key words

dynamic – a changing load

load – the forces acting on a structure

member – a part of a structure

static – a constant load

SUMMARY

- Compression forces are squashing forces.
- Materials must be chosen to resist these forces in order to make a successful structure.
- Structures like bridges and buildings are complex so it may not be a simple task to identify which forces are present.

SUMMARY *activity*

Take three blocks of materials about 50 mm square: use modelling clay, polystyrene foam and balsa wood. Stand on each one, and then measure their thickness. Make a chart to show how each withstands the compression forces.

61 Tension

In this section of the book you will learn the following things:
- what tension forces are;
- how tension forces affect materials;
- how materials are chosen to resist tensile forces.

Stretching materials

Tension forces are stretching forces – they are trying to pull the materials apart. All materials, when put into tension, will increase their length – even materials such as steel. If the load is increased, the stretching stops and the material will eventually break or fail (Fig 1).

Q1 What parts of a child's swing are in tension?

You will have noticed when you carry a heavy plastic carrier bag from the supermarket that the handles, which are in tension due to the weight of your groceries, will stretch. In stretching they get thinner but seldom break. Plastics, when stretched, often become stronger than the unstretched plastic. Materials are tested in machines which measure gradually increased load on the material. This is called measuring the **tensile strength**. Steel has a high tensile strength, but concrete is very poor. Many suspension bridges have steel

▲ **Fig 1** Tensile forces.

▼ **Fig 2** Clifton Suspension Bridge, Bristol.

wires holding up the roadway; these wires are in tension and are usually anchored into rocks or large blocks of concrete on the banks (Fig 2). Steel wire is really strong. When materials are used in tension, they are often in rope, wire or flat **strip** form. These forms are very poor in compression as they tend to **buckle** or bend drastically. Concrete is poor in tension, torsion or bending, so is often reinforced by casting it with steel rods inside. These rods are held in tension until the concrete is set. This results in a much improved material (Fig 3).

Q2 Why do you think steel wire is used in suspension bridges rather than solid steel?

Q3 How are reinforced concrete beams made?

In textiles, some materials are better then others in tension and are therefore used to make handles for sports bags, belts and straps for clothes. Most of these materials are made from plastics such as nylon or polypropylene. In an accident, car seat belts would be in tension – the material as it stretches gives a more cushioned effect.

▲ **Fig 3** Reinforced concrete used in the Severn Bridge.

Key words

buckle – to bend irregularly
strips – flat narrow sheets of thin materials
tensile strength – the load which a material can withstand
tension force – a pulling force

SUMMARY

■ Materials that are being stretched are said to be in tension.
■ Tensile forces are trying to pull the material apart.
■ All materials being stretched get longer until a limit is reached.
■ Materials are selected for their characteristics.

SUMMARY
activity

Cut two strips of plastic from a polythene carrier bag: one strip across the bag and one from the length of the bag. For each strip, use two bulldog clips, one on either end, hang it up and put weights on until the plastic breaks. Are there differences in the way the strips look?

62 Torsion

In this section of the book you will learn the following things:
- what torsion forces are;
- how torsion forces affect materials;
- where torsion forces are found.

Twisting materials

▲ **Fig 1** Torsion.

Torsion is twisting. It can be what happens to a screwdriver shaft when you are tightening a screw (Fig 1). A bolt when being turned with a spanner is being subjected to torsional load, also called **torque**. Often it is very important to tighten bolts to the correct load so that they are not overstressed. This is done using a calibrated spanner called a **torque wrench**. When a car is being driven, the power from the engine is transmitted to the back wheels by the prop shaft (Fig 2). This shaft is being twisted by the engine as the back wheels are resisting being turned. Everything which is being rotated, either by motors or human power, has some parts which are being subjected to torsion (Fig 3).

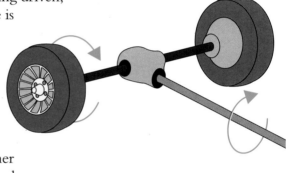

▲ **Fig 2** A car drive system.

Q1 Name two parts on a bicycle which are in torsion when its being ridden.

When subjected to forces, all materials stretch until a certain point is reached, so engine components are constantly twisted and stretched, and then return to their original shape. This constant movement hardens the material which will eventually fail.

▲ **Fig 3** A shaft in torsion.

Torsion is often used to make a form of spring called a torsion bar. If one end of a steel rod is held fixed and the other end connected to a moving part, then when the rod is twisted and let go, it springs back to its original position provided it has not gone beyond its **elastic limit**. Common uses include a spring to close a gate (Fig 4) and car suspensions.

Q2 How can springs be made using torsion?

Q3 Why do materials which are constantly in use sometimes fail?

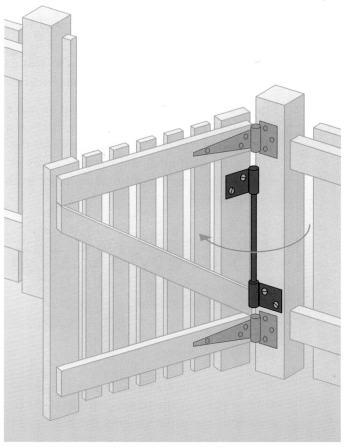

▲ **Fig 4** A gate-closer torsion spring.

Key words

elastic limit – when materials are stretched, they return to their original length, unless they have been stretched beyond the elastic limit

torque – the force of twisting

torque wrench – a spanner on which you can set how much torque you apply

torsion – twisting

SUMMARY

■ Torsion is a twisting force. It occurs for example when screws and bolts are tightened.

■ Torsion occurs in parts of any mechanisms which have rotary movement.

■ Torsion bars are used as effective, strong springs for closing gates or in car suspensions.

SUMMARY
activity

Use a 200 mm piece of steel rod under 1 mm in diameter and bend a right angle 20 mm from each end. Hold one end still and twist the other end. If you do not twist it too much, it will spring back to its original position. If you twist it too much, you will pass the material's elastic limit and it will not spring back.

63 Shear

In this section of the book you will learn the following things:
- what shear forces are;
- how we use shear forces to cut things;
- some examples of where shear forces occur.

Shear acts across a material, trying to make one part slide across another. When a screw holds up a shelf bracket on a wall, the weight of the shelf and its contents are trying to push downwards the part of the screw that is not in the wall. It is trying to slice the screw across its width. The force is parallel to the wall. There is no bending taking place as the load is applied as close to the wall as possible (Fig 1).

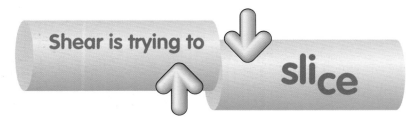

▲ **Fig 1** Shear forces.

If two pieces of metal are riveted together, then trying to pull or push either or both parts of the metal will put shear forces on the **rivets**. When you use scissors to cut paper or card, the blades of the scissors are forcing the paper to break, by forcing one side of the cut upwards and the other side downwards (Fig 2). The paper or card is being put into shear. Guillotines, tin snips and can-openers all cut by using this method.

▶ **Fig 2** Scissors cutting paper.

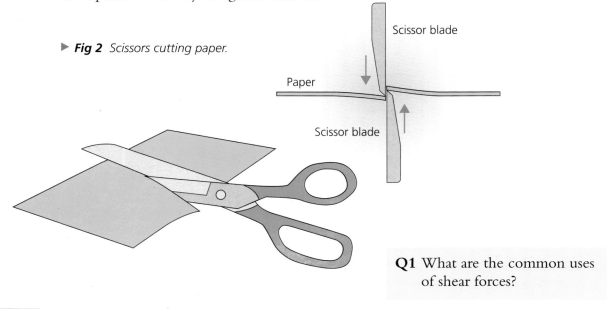

Q1 What are the common uses of shear forces?

▲ *Fig 3* Mountaineer's fixings.

Climbers connect their ropes to bolts which are hammered into rocks and then rely on these bolts not failing due to the shear loads put on them (Fig 3). Devices such as these, which are designed to be used in shear, are made from materials such as **high tensile steel** or other alloys.

Q2 When mountaineers climb mountains, where do shear forces come into play?

However, when rivets are used, they are quite soft because they need both to be hammered over and to suit the characteristics of the material they are being used to join.

Cold chisels are used in the workshop to cut sheet metal by shearing it against the jaws of a vice.

Seat belt fixings in cars are designed not to break under tremendous shear loads in accidents.

Q3 Why is high tensile steel often used for bolts which are subjected to shear forces?

Key words

high tensile steel – a very strong type of steel

rivets – metal fixing devices which hold sheets of metal together

shear – a force which acts across a material

SUMMARY

- Shear force acts across a material, e.g. in screws and bolts it acts across the diameter of the screw and tries to 'slice it'.
- Screws, nails and bolts are all designed to resist shear forces by the correct choice of materials.
- Shelf brackets rely on screws to resist shear and hold up the shelves.

SUMMARY
activity

In a block of wood drill a small hole about one centimetre deep, just big enough to take a matchstick. Push in a matchstick. Using weights hung from the matchstick, test to see which position on the matchstick will take the greatest weight. Is it close to the wooden block or nearer to the end of the matchstick? Why is this?

64 Bending

In this section of the book you will learn the following things:
- what happens when bending occurs;
- how to make structures stiffer;
- how beams are used.

Bending occurs when a force is applied to a structure whilst one or both ends are fixed. The structure deflects according to the amount of force applied to it. All structures can be made to bend but how much depends on their **cross-section**. The top section of a beam, when it bends, is in compression and the lower section is in tension (Fig 1). If you take a cardboard cornflake box, it is easier to bend when lying flat than if it is on its edge.

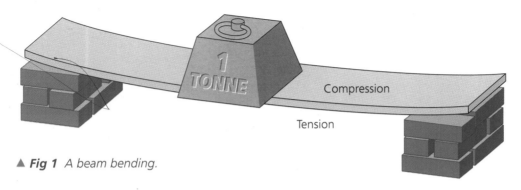

▲ **Fig 1** A beam bending.

Q1 How can you reduce the amount of bending in a beam?

A beam is a structure which is supported at both ends and spans a gap. Beams are used for bridges and roof spans in buildings such as sports halls. A **cantilever** is a structure which is supported only at one end, such as a crane or the roof of a rugby or football stand (Fig 2). Sometimes roadways are built on pillars with the surface cantilevered from the pillar. In the cases of both the roof and the roadway, they have to be designed to resist bending but this depends on the materials used and on their cross-sections.

◀ **Fig 2** Cantilevered balconies.

Aircraft wings are cantilevers and are designed to be **stiff** yet very lightweight (Fig 3). Structures have to support their own weight, so the lighter they can be made, the better. Stiffness can be achieved by triangulating structures, by reinforcing or by making them of box sections. Beams which are of rectangular section are stiffer if the vertical part of the section is longer than the breadth. Some beams can be made very lightweight. **Buckling** is irregular bending, for example, what happens when you stand on a soft drinks can (Fig 4).

▲ **Fig 3** A cantilevered aircraft wing.

◀ **Fig 4** Buckling.

Q2 A cantilevered beam can be found in most swimming pools. What is it?

Q3 How could you make a beam from a sheet of A4 paper?

Key words

buckling – irregular bending

cantilever – a beam supported only at one end

cross-section – the cut face showing when you cut through something

stiffness – the ability to resist bending

SUMMARY

■ Beams are designed to support structures.

■ When subjected to forces all structures will bend or move.

■ Beams are structures which are usually supported at both ends; cantilevered beams are supported at one end.

■ Beams can be stiffened by triangulation, reinforcing or by using various sections.

SUMMARY *activity*

Use a block of foam 400 mm × 60 mm × 50 mm. Draw centre lines along the length and width of each side. Bending this beam will show the surfaces which are in compression or tension.

65 Building model structures

In this section of the book you will learn the following things:
- the reasons for modelling structures;
- the materials you can use;
- testing model structures.

Building materials

One way of seeing how structures really work is to build models. This can be to explore how real structures are built, or you can test your structures to see how strong you can make them and what you can do to them to make them stronger. There are kits which you can use to make models, and some of these will allow you to measure the loads on each member (Fig 1). The easiest structures to make in school are frame and shell structures. Frame structures are made from strip materials such as drinking straws or

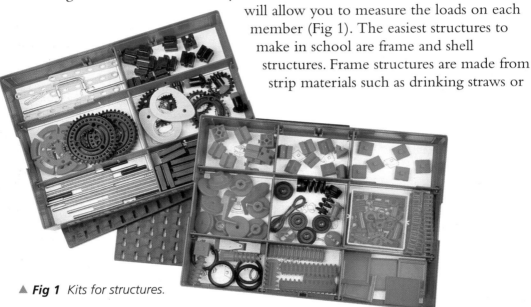

▲ **Fig 1** *Kits for structures.*

uncooked spaghetti which can be glued together using either PVA glue or, better still, a glue gun (Fig 2). The glue gun allows you to build models quickly as you do not have to wait for the glue to dry.

If you look at real structures such as cranes and bridges, you will see that they are often built using lots of triangles. This **triangulation** can make really strong, rigid structures which are very light.

◄ **Fig 2** *Framed structure made from drinking straws.*

> **Q1** What are two common uses of a framed structure?

▲ *Fig 3* *Triangulation using struts on a sports car chassis.*

You can test this by building a simple box from straws or spaghetti and pushing one corner. The box will distort easily, but if you now glue members from corner to corner of the box, it will become very difficult to distort it. These parts are called **struts**, and the process is called triangulation (Fig 3). In this type of structure every **member** is important – if one breaks, it usually results in the failure of the whole structure. Instead of struts which are in compression, you can often use **ties** which are always in tension. Try replacing the struts in the model with ties made of cotton or thin string.

Shell structures are usually built from sheet material, and you can build these using paper or card. If you stand on a soft-drinks can, which is extremely light, it will support your weight. By folding sheets of paper and by putting **corrugations** into it, you can make shell structures which will support heavy loads (Fig 4).

Q2 Why does triangulation help make structures stronger?

▲ *Fig 4* *Shell structure model.*

Q3 What are two examples of a shell structure which you see everyday?

Key words

corrugation – putting a series of folds into paper or card

member – an individual part of a structure

struts – rigid members used in compression

ties – flexible members used in tension

triangulation – triangles are the strongest elements of a structure and cannot be deformed

SUMMARY

- Modelling using straws, spaghetti, lolly sticks and a glue gun for framed structures, and folded paper or card for shell structures, can be useful ways of experimenting with structures.
- Testing to destruction can be carried out by loading your structures. You must then carefully examine how the structure failed.

SUMMARY *activity*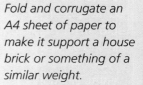

Fold and corrugate an A4 sheet of paper to make it support a house brick or something of a similar weight.

66 Loads

In this section of the book you will learn the following things:
- what static loads are;
- what dynamic loads are;
- how static and dynamic loads affect structures.

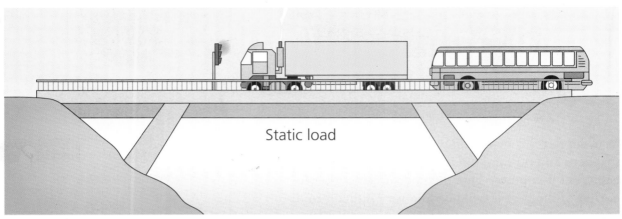

▲ **Fig 1** *A stationary lorry means a static load.*

Moving or stationary loads

If you imagine a bridge with a lorry stopped on it, then the lorry's weight will be fixed and not changing and the load on the bridge is **static** (Fig 1). If the lorry drives across a bridge and other lorries follow, then the load will change as more and more lorries move on and off it. The load in this case is changing all the time – this is a **dynamic** load (Fig 2). All structures can take greater static loading than dynamic loading. If you are trying to snap a stick by standing on it, often it will not break. Usually, the next thing you try is to jump on it and it breaks. In the first case you were trying a static load and in the second, a dynamic load.

Q1 What type of load are books on a bookshelf applying?

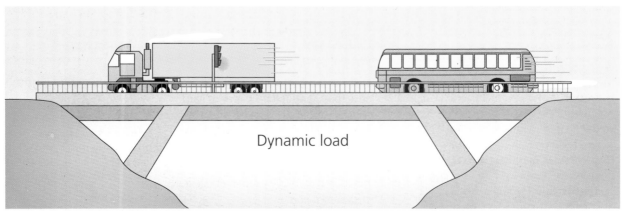

▲ **Fig 2** *Moving lorries mean a dynamic load.*

All structures are subjected to static and dynamic loads. A building has static forces acting on it: its own weight, the roof, the floors, the furniture inside. When the wind blows, especially if it is a very tall building like a skyscraper, then dynamic forces try to push the building over. These forces will be constantly changing depending on the strength of the wind and how gusty it is.

▶ **Fig 3** *Distributed load acting in a drinks can.*

Q2 What type of force does a karate player use to break a piece of wood?

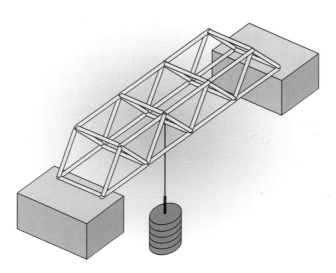

▲ **Fig 4** *Loading a model structure with a point load.*

Q3 What type of loads would you expect on a sailing ship's sails?

Being aware of loads

When designing structures, designers have to be aware of these loads as dynamic loads can have several times the effect of static loads. Forces sometimes act on a single place, called a **point** load, or they can be spread over an area – this is called a **distributed** load. A soft drinks can is a shell structure and when unopened, it has a distributed load acting on it due to the gas pressure in the can (Fig 3). If you drop it onto a hard surface, much higher dynamic loads come into play and it will split. When you test your models, you will usually use static loads. This means carefully loading the structure without jerky movements (Fig 4). One way is to use sand or water as the weight and gradually pour it into a suspended container so that the weight increases steadily.

Key words

distributed – acting over the whole area
dynamic – moving
point – acting at a single point
static – stationary

SUMMARY

- Static loads are stationary loads; dynamic loads are changing loads and have a much greater effect on structures.
- Point loads act at one point.
- Distributed loads act over a surface.
- Designers have to be aware of these forces when designing all types of structures.

SUMMARY
activity

Make a light structure from drinking straws that will span a 300 mm gap and which will just support a tennis ball. Drop the tennis ball from a height of 300 mm onto the structure. Record what happens and explain why.

67 **Understanding circuit diagrams**

In this section of the book you will learn the following things:
- how to read circuit diagrams;
- why component symbols are used;
- how to build a circuit from the circuit diagram.

Why use circuit diagrams?

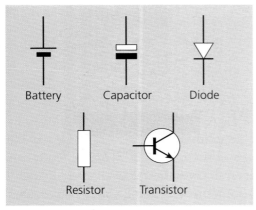

▲ **Fig 1** Some circuit symbols.

Circuit diagrams show you the connections between **components** in an electronic circuit. They do not show what the actual parts look like or their size. The components are shown as symbols which tell you what type they are and how many connections they have (Fig 1). It would take space and be confusing to use real drawings of components. Those with lots of connections, such as integrated circuits, have them numbered but are not always shown in the right order. Transistors, for example, have three leads, called emitter, base and collector. These are shown on the diagram as a symbol (Fig 2). The electronic symbols are listed on page 213.

Q1 Why are symbols used instead of pictures of the components?

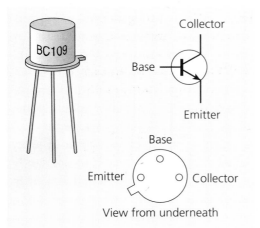

▲ **Fig 2** A transistor and its symbol.

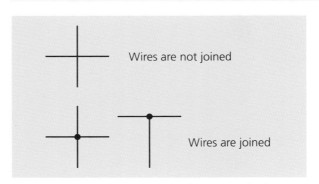

▲ **Fig 3** Unconnected wires and connected wires.

Reading a circuit diagram

If, on the circuit diagram, you see two wires crossing each other, they are not connected together in the real circuit. If you see wires crossing and there is a round black dot where they cross, then these wires are joined (Fig 3). There are usually two lines: one across the top, and one across the bottom of the diagram. These are the supply lines, where the positive and negative leads from the battery are connected. Any inputs are usually shown at the left of the diagram and outputs at the right.

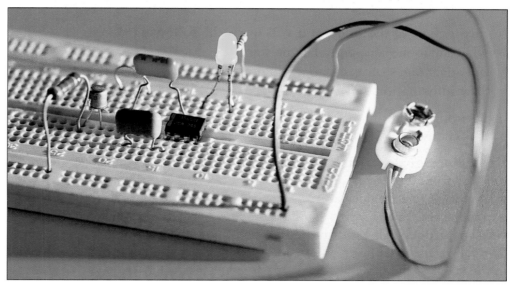

▲ **Fig 4** *A prototype board.*

There are several ways to read the circuit diagram and make the circuit using real components. You can lay the components out on paper and neatly draw the connections between them. Then use a **prototype board** which lets you push the legs of the components into connecting holes and build up the circuit easily without soldering. If you want to change them, you just unplug them (Fig 4). When the circuit works, you can transfer the components to a circuit board. Another way is to use a computer program such as *Crocodile Clips,* which lets you copy the circuit diagram to test if it works. You can use the computer package to automatically design a **PCB**. Once the PCB is made, the components can then be soldered onto it.

Q2 What are the two lines at the top and bottom of a circuit?

Q3 Why would you use a prototype board to build circuits?

Key words

components – parts of a circuit like transistors, diodes, etc

PCB – printed circuit board

prototype board – a plastic board with holes allowing components to be plugged in

SUMMARY

■ Circuit diagrams are used to show you the connections between the components in a circuit.

■ Symbols are used to show the different types of component – you should learn some of these.

■ Lines which cross on the diagram are not connected in the actual circuit. Where wires connect, they are shown by a black dot joining them on the diagram.

SUMMARY activity

Make a diagram using drawings of the components in the Darlington Pair circuit to show how they are connected together.

68 Analogue and digital signals

In this section of the book you will learn the following things:
- what analogue and digital signals are;
- the advantages of using an analogue or digital signal;
- how information can be transmitted.

In electronics there are signals which transmit information between the various parts of the system. These signals can be in two forms: either analogue or digital.

Analogue signals vary in **amplitude** – if you have a 9 volt analogue signal it can vary from 0 to 9 volts, and every value in between. If you speak into a microphone, you produce a small signal; if you speak louder, it will increase. If you then shout, a larger signal will be produced (Fig 1). The main problem with analogue signals is that if they are transmitted over long distances, such as by radio or in a telephone system, they soon get distorted. The information is in the value of the signal and this can be gradually reduced by the effect of **interference**. We still use analogue signals for many things, the sound coming from the speakers of your TV is produced by analogue signals.

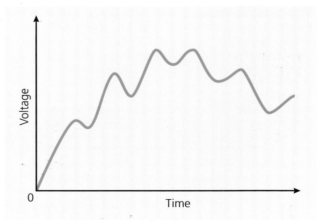

▲ *Fig 1* An analogue signal.

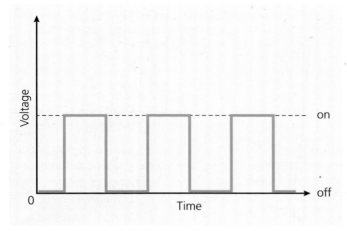

▲ *Fig 2* A digital signal.

Digital signals always have the same amplitude; the information is chopped into small parts called pulses (Fig 2). Unlike the analogue signal which can be any amplitude, the digital signal has only two states: on or off. The states are referred to as **high** for on and **low** for off; sometimes this is also called 1 or 0.

Q1 How do digital signals differ from analogue signals?

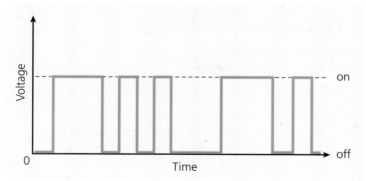

▲ *Fig 3* *Changing the pulse width.*

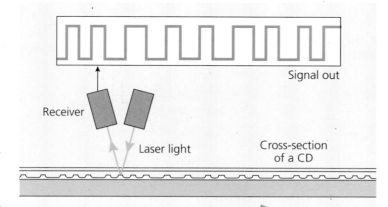

Receiver

Laser light

Cross-section of a CD

Signal out

▲ *Fig 4* *The digital information on a CD.*

When transmitted long distances, it is easy to repair a digital signal if it should get weaker as it is only on or off. It can be easily amplified to make it clearer and to get rid of interference. The information is transmitted by the signal being on or off and by making the **pulse width** longer or shorter (Fig 3).

When you switch a switch on and off, you are producing a digital pulse. It can only have two states, on or off, and cannot be anywhere between on or off. This is why switches are often used as sensors in systems. Computers and **CD**s only use digital signals (Fig 4).

Q2 What is the name of an early form of digital signal which used a flashing lamp or buzzer to transmit information?

Q3 Why are digital signals less affected by interference?

Key words

amplitude – height of a signal

analogue signal – a signal which is changing in amplitude

CD – compact disk

digital signal – a signal which has two states: on or off

high – on, 1

interference – noise which stops information getting through

low – off, 0

pulse width – the time a digital signal is on or off

SUMMARY

■ Information is transmitted using analogue and digital voltages.

■ Analogue voltages vary continually, whereas digital voltages are either on or off.

■ Analogue signals can suffer from interference, but digital signals can be easily restored if distorted.

SUMMARY activity

Draw a diagram to show how digital information is stored on a CD.

69 Capacitors

In this section of the book you will learn the following things:
- how to identify the different types of capacitor;
- what the various types are used for;
- how to find the values of capacitors as used in series and parallel.

Capacitors store charge and are used in most electronic circuits. The charge gradually leaks away with time; some capacitors are better than others and **leak** less.

Q1 What do capacitors do?

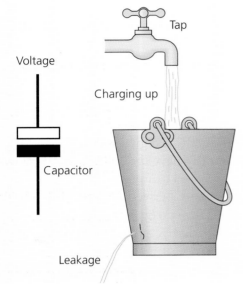

▲ **Fig 1** Capacitor and water analogy.

The operation of capacitors can be compared with a small bucket with a hole in it. The water is the electrons filling the capacitor. As the water leaks out of the bucket, it represents the capacitor discharging (Fig 1). When used in timer circuits, capacitors are charged through a resistor until a certain voltage is sensed. Larger capacitors will take longer to charge. The formula for working out the **time constant** is:

$$t = c \times r \text{ where } t \text{ is in seconds, } c \text{ is in farads, } r \text{ is in ohms.}$$

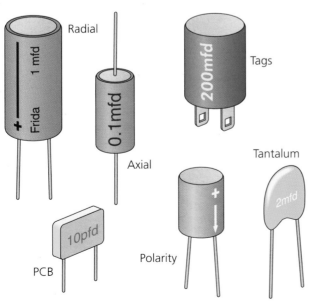

▲ **Fig 2** Different types of capacitors.

Capacity values can be measured in microfarads (mfd), picofarads (pfd) and nanofarads (nfd). Some capacitors are **polarised**, which means that they have to be fitted the correct way around. They usually have markings to show the positive connection: + signs, red or black marks, stripes or arrows. When selecting them, you need to know the value, the working voltage, the type and the fitting (Fig 2). Some are made to be plugged into printed circuit boards, some have wire ends and some have solder tags. The types are known by the materials from which they are made.

Electrolytic – these are large value, polarised capacitors, which are not very accurate.

Tantalum – physically very small capacitors with high value. They are always low voltage and polarised.

Polyester – high values in small spaces.

Polycarbon – cheap, general purpose.

Paper – very accurate, low leakage, expensive.

Ceramic – high quality.

Mica – small, accurate values.

The **working voltage** is the maximum voltage which can be applied to the capacitor; it is very important not to exceed this voltage as it will damage the capacitor.

For capacitors in series (Fig 3), the working voltages add together:

$$\frac{1}{C_{total}} = \frac{1}{C_1} + \frac{1}{C_2} + \frac{1}{C_3} + \dots$$

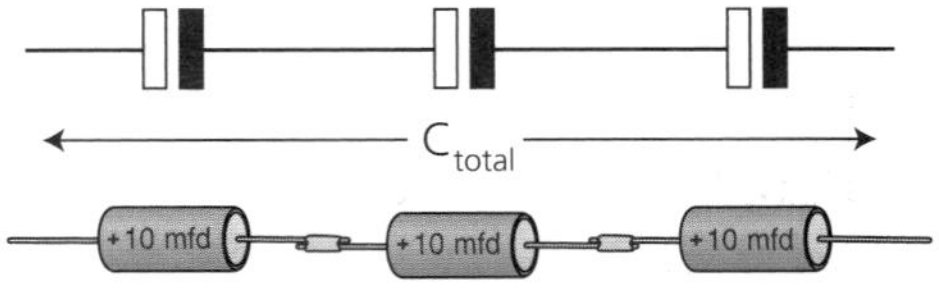

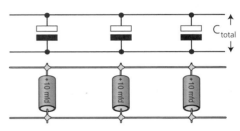

▲ **Fig 3** Capacitors in series.

Capacitors in parallel (Fig 4), each working voltage must be greater then the voltage applied:

$$C_{total} = C_1 + C_2 + C_3 + \dots$$

▲ **Fig 4** Capacitors in parallel.

Q2 Why is it important not to go above the working voltage on a capacitor?

Q3 If you wanted a large value capacitor for a circuit, which type would you use?

Key words

capacitor – a device which stores charge

leakage – the charge in a capacitor drains away over time

polarised – must be fitted the correct way round

time constant – time taken to charge a capacitor

working voltage – the maximum voltage that can be applied to a capacitor

SUMMARY

■ Capacitors are used in electronic circuits, often in timer circuits. There is a wide range of different types, mostly called by the name of the material from which they are made.

■ Some can only work in circuits the correct way around – they are polarised.

■ They have a working voltage which should not be exceeded.

SUMMARY *activity*

Make up the timer circuit (Fig 5) and change the value of the capacitor to see what difference it makes to the time.

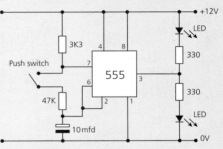

▲ **Fig 5** A timer circuit using capacitors.

70 Resistors

In this section of the book you will learn the following things:
- how to identify the values of resistors;
- how to work out the values when they are in series and parallel;
- the different types of fixed and variable resistors.

Resistors are usually made of carbon film, but some are wirewound. They have coloured bands which tell you their value in ohms (Fig 1). A value over one thousand ohms, is called a **kilohm** and written as 4K7 (4700 ohms) or 47K (47 000 ohms); over one million ohms is a **megohm** and written as 3M9 (3 900 000 ohms) or 22M (22 000 000 ohms).

Q1 What do the coloured bands stand for on resistors?

▲ **Fig 1** The coloured bands on a resistor.

The M or K takes the place of the decimal point. One coloured band tells you the tolerance of the resistor, normally 1%, 2%, 5% or 10%, so a 1K 5% resistor will have a value which lies between 950 and 1050 ohms. This means that you need less resistors to cover the full range of values. There is a colour code chart on page 211. To work out the values of resistors used in series or parallel, you must use the following formulae.

When resistors are in series (Fig 2), their values add together:

$$\text{Resistance}_{\text{total}} = R_1 + R_2 + R_3 + \ldots$$

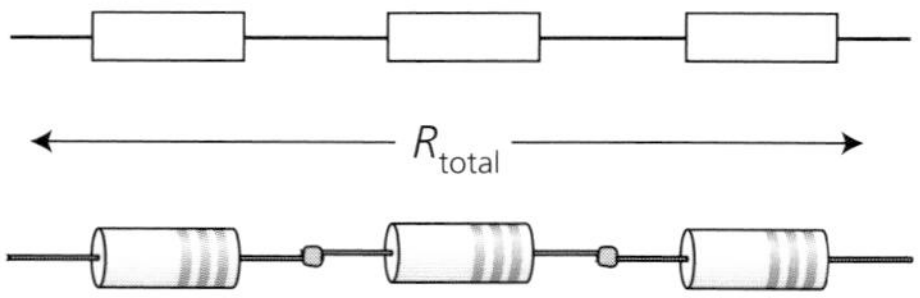

▲ **Fig 2** Resistors in series.

When resistors are used in parallel (Fig 3), their total value decreases:

$$\text{Resistance}_{\text{total}} = \frac{1}{R_1} + \frac{1}{R_2} + \frac{1}{R_3} + \ldots$$

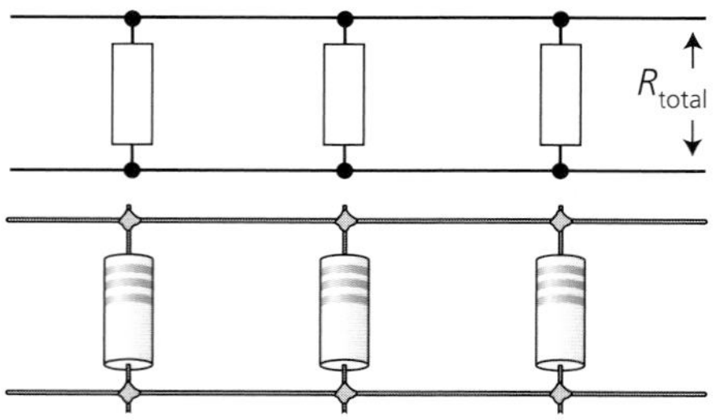

▲ **Fig 3** Resistors in parallel.

Variable resistors or **potentiometers** have wipers which run on a track. The wiper is connected to a shaft on which a control knob can be mounted. A **preset resistor** is designed to be adjusted using a screwdriver. (Fig 4). Variable resistors can have linear tracks where the resistance value changes linearly when the wiper is moved, and logarithmic when the resistance changes progressively around the track. These words are often printed as **Lin** or **Log** on the body of the resistor.

▲ *Fig 4* *Variable and preset resistors.*

LDRs are light-dependent resistors which change their resistance when light falls on them – they are used in light sensing projects.

Q2 How do you adjust a preset resistor?

Q3 What is the range of values covered by a 1K 20% tolerance resistor?

Thermistors change resistance with temperature. If they increase their resistance as temperature increases, they have a positive temperature coefficient (**PTC**). If they increase their resistance as the temperature decreases, they have a negative temperature coefficient (**NTC**).

Key words

kilohm – one thousand ohms

LDR – light-dependent resistor

Lin – linear resistance track

Log – logarithmic resistance track

megohm – one million ohms

NTC – negative temperature coefficient

potentiometer – another name for a variable resistor

preset resistor – a screwdriver operated variable resistor

PTC – positive temperature coefficient

thermistors – temperature dependant resistors

SUMMARY

■ Resistors have coloured bands to let you know the value.
■ They also have a tolerance value. This means that not every value of resistor has to be stocked.
■ The value of variable resistors can be changed by turning the shaft.
■ Some resistors can change their values when light or temperature changes.

SUMMARY activity

Draw a colour picture of ten different value resistors and their bands. Choose the values you use most frequently.

71 Switches

In this section of the book you will learn the following things:

- the range of switches available for project work;
- how to choose them;
- how to make your own pressure and tilt switches.

Switches are used to interrupt the current flow in a circuit. They can be homemade provided safe low voltages are used. There are lots of types, including toggle, push-button, slider, micro, reed, magnetic and tilt. The choice of switch depends on you and your project. You can make your choice from the manufacturers' catalogues.

Q1 What do switches do in a circuit?

Switches can have different electrical contacts as well as different operating methods. When you order a switch, you need to know the voltage and current it has to handle, the type of button, toggle, etc. to operate it and also the type of contacts. These are listed below:

Single pole single throw (**SPST**) switches a circuit on or off (Fig 1).

Single pole double throw (**SPDT**) switches one circuit between two connections (Fig 2).

Double pole single throw (**DPST**) switches two separate circuits on or off (Fig 3). These are like two separate on/off switches in one component.

Double pole double throw (**DPDT**) switches two separate circuits between two connections each. This switch is very useful for reversing motors (Fig 4).

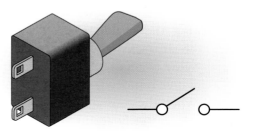

▲ **Fig 1** Single pole single throw switch.

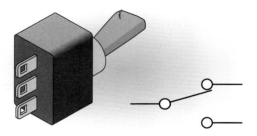

▲ **Fig 2** Single pole double throw switch.

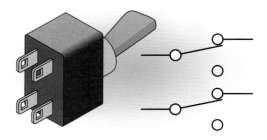

▲ **Fig 3** Double pole single throw switch.

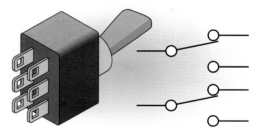

▲ **Fig 4** Double pole double throw switch.

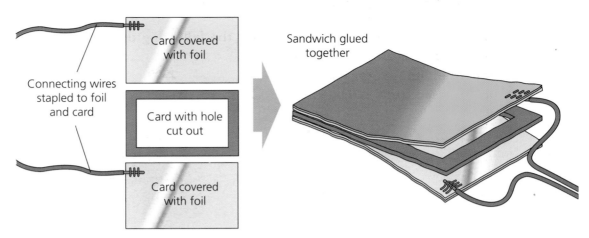

Connecting wires
stapled to foil
and card

Card covered
with foil

Card with hole
cut out

Card covered
with foil

Sandwich glued
together

▲ **Fig 5** *A homemade
pressure switch.*

Microswitches and tilt switches

Microswitches and tilt switches are really useful for your projects and can be
input sensors for control projects. Microswitches have buttons or levers which
need only a very light pressure to operate – they can be used as sensors of
buggies. Tilt switches have a container with a little mercury bead inside –
when you tilt the container, the mercury shorts out two contacts causing the
switch to operate. They are useful for door sensors. You can make your own tilt
and pressure switches from plastic film containers, card and aluminium foil. The
tilt switch can be a plastic film container with two thick wires pushed through
the bottom and a ball of aluminium cooking foil instead of the mercury.
A pressure switch can be made of three sheets of card, the two outer ones
having foil glued to their inner
surfaces and leads stapled to the foil.
The middle sheet has a window cut
in it. When the three are fixed
together the two pieces of foil are
held apart by the window until
pressure is applied (Fig 5).

Q2 What do you need to know
when selecting a switch to use?

Q3 What type of switches would
you need to act as sensors on
a buggy?

Key words

DPDT – double pole
double throw
DPST – double pole
single throw
SPDT – single pole
double throw
SPST – single pole
single throw

SUMMARY

■ There are a wide variety of switches available for
your projects, both in how they operate and their
electrical characteristics.
■ They all interrupt or connect current flowing in a
circuit.
■ Several types can be easily made.

SUMMARY
activity

*Make a pressure switch,
as in Fig 5, to use in a
project.*

72 Logic gates

In this section of the book you will learn the following things:
- **what gates are used for;**
- **what the different types of gate do;**
- **how to read truth tables.**

Combining inputs

Sometimes in electronics, we want to use a series of inputs to make something happen so we choose **logic gates**. We might want an output from a circuit or system when one input is on and another is off. We usually use integrated circuits which may contain four gates in the same package (Fig 1). Each gate has two to four inputs. They are circuits with several inputs and these can be switched on or off, i.e. logic state 1 (**high**) or 0 (**low**). They are called AND, OR and NOT.

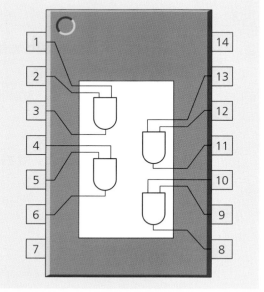

▲ *Fig 1* *An integrated circuit containing four gates.*

Q1 Why are gates needed?

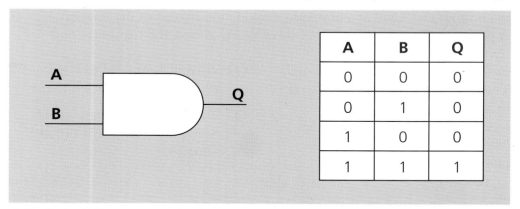

A	B	Q
0	0	0
0	1	0
1	0	0
1	1	1

▲ *Fig 2* *An AND gate and truth table.*

An AND gate will only produce an output when all of its inputs are high, i.e. logic state 1. We say, when input 1 AND input 2 AND input 3, etc. are high, that an output occurs (Fig 2).

With an OR gate, an output will happen when input 1 OR input 2 OR input 3 are present (Fig 3).

With a NOT gate, an output is present when an input is not present and vice versa (Fig 4).

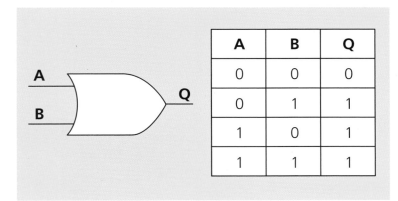

A	B	Q
0	0	0
0	1	1
1	0	1
1	1	1

▲ **Fig 3** *An OR gate and truth table.*

A	Q
1	0 .
0	1

▲ **Fig 4** *A NOT gate and truth table.*

Truth tables

To simplify your understanding of what each gate does, there are truth tables which show the inputs as A, B, C, etc. The inputs and outputs are shown as being on or off, i.e. 1 or 0. You can read across the table to see what the output will be for different inputs being switched on. There are two main types of integrated circuits available: **TTL** which requires a 5 volt supply and **CMOS** which works with 3 to 15 volts. Both have their advantages, but CMOS is probably better for school use. There are three other gates which you will learn about later – NAND, NOR and XOR. You may find that your school has some electronics kits with logic chips or you can use a computer package which will let you model logic circuits. When you are using diagrams of logic circuits, remember that the supply voltage connections are usually not shown.

Q2 If your project has two buttons which must be pressed at the same time to start it, what type of gate would you need?

Q3 What do we use truth tables for?

Key words

CMOS – complementary metal oxide semiconductor
gate – a device which switches depending upon its inputs
high – a 1 logic state, voltage present
logic – representing signals at 0 or 1 states
low – a 0 logic state, no voltage present
TTL – transistor transistor logic

SUMMARY

■ Logic gates are devices which can be used to combine signals to produce outputs. There are six types – AND, OR, NOT, NAND, NOR and XOR.
■ They are digital devices so they respond to signals which are logic state 1 or 0, i.e. high or low.
■ They can be combined to produce more complicated circuits.
■ They can be TTL or CMOS types.

SUMMARY activity

Design the logic circuit for a simple game where a buzzer sounds when two things happen at the same time.

73 Semiconductors

In this section of the book you will learn the following things:
- what a semiconductor is;
- how transistors and diodes work;
- how to use the Darlington Pair circuit.

Semiconductors are important components such as transistors, diodes and light-emitting diodes. They decrease their resistance when hot so they can be damaged or even destroyed as they heat up. Some need to be fixed to a metal **heatsink** to keep them cool. They all need to be connected to the correct polarity to prevent damage. They are made of **P** and **N type** materials.

Q1 Why do transistors sometimes need heatsinks?

Diodes

Diodes are components which allow current to flow in one direction only. They have two leads called the anode and the cathode (kathode). For current to flow through a diode the anode needs to be connected to positive and the cathode to negative (Fig 1).

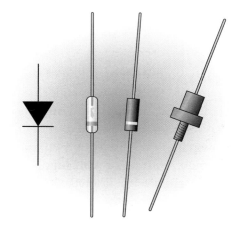

▲ **Fig 1** Diodes.

Thyristors are diodes with an extra connection called a gate. They will not conduct until a small current is applied to the gate. They can only be switched off by removing the current passing through them. This is called latching.

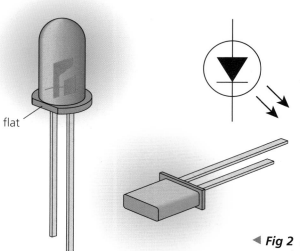

flat

Light-emitting diodes are diodes which emit light when current flows through them. They must be used with a resistor in series with them otherwise they will pass too much current and be damaged. The value of the resistor is between 390 and 470 ohms for a 9 volt circuit. **LEDs** come in a few colours and are used as indicator lamps. Some will flash automatically (Fig 2).

◀ **Fig 2** Light-emitting diodes.

Transistors

Transistors are made of three sections of semiconductor P or N type material called the base, the collector and the emitter. These sections or layers can be arranged as P–N–P or N–P–N. PNP transistors need a negative supply to the collector, and the NPN types need a positive supply line (Fig 3).

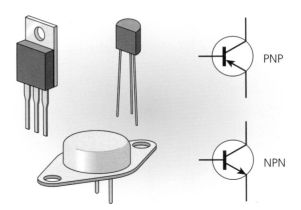

▲ **Fig 3** *Transistors.*

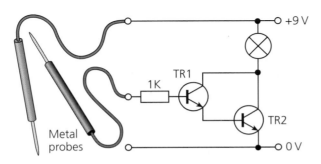

▲ **Fig 4** *Darlington Pair using two probes.*

Transistors can act like a switch and be on or off, or can act as an amplifier. In the Darlington Pair, the two transistors act like a switch when the base of the first transistor is connected through a resistor to the positive line – just touching the two probes will switch on the lamp (Fig 4). Both transistors are NPN devices. Some transistors have mounting plates which allow them to be fixed to heatsinks (Fig 5). The Darlington Pair circuit can be used in many project ideas.

Q2 Why do light-emitting diodes require a series resistor?

Q3 What are the three connections on a transistor?

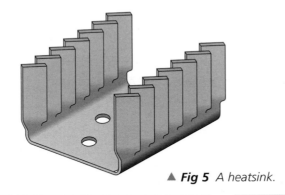

▲ **Fig 5** *A heatsink.*

Key words

diode – a device which passes current in one direction

heatsink – a metal plate used to remove heat from semiconductors

LEDs – light-emitting diodes

N type – negative type semiconductor

P type – positive type semiconductor

semiconductor – a silicon- or germanium-based material

SUMMARY

■ Semiconductors are easily damaged by heat and incorrect polarity.

■ They are made from combinations of P and N materials.

■ LEDs are indicator lamps and must be used with a series resistor.

SUMMARY activity

Use an LED, battery and a series resistor to make a simple continuity tester.

74 Integrated circuits

In this section of the book you will learn the following things:
- what integrated circuits do;
- how they are made;
- how to use them and prevent damage to them.

Integrated circuits (ICs) are made using very small pieces of silicon material on which tiny circuits are etched. The circuits are drawn in large scale and then reduced by photographic methods. They are less than one millimetre square and can contain many hundreds of thousands of transistors. The connections are made using very fine wires. The whole **chip** and its wires are encased in plastic with metal pins coming from the sides. These allow the chip to be soldered into a printed circuit board, or plugged into a **socket**. Chips have from four pins to over 64 pins depending on how complex they are.

There is a small dot or shaped notch at one end to show where pin one is (Fig 1). Integrated circuits can be damaged by heat when soldering, so it is a good idea to use sockets. These can be soldered into the board and the chip plugged into them. This allows you easily to change chips that might be faulty (Fig 2).

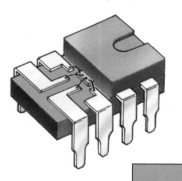

▲ **Fig 1** A cutaway view of an integrated circuit.

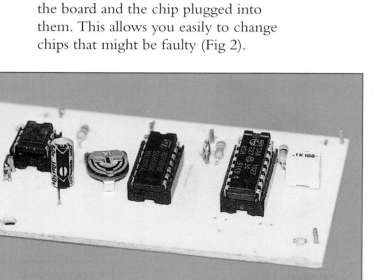

▲ **Fig 2** ICs in sockets.

Because it is made of semiconductor materials, it is important that the supply voltages to the integrated circuit are connected the correct way round. If not, the integrated circuit can be damaged instantly. They generally take very little current, so can be used with batteries.

Q1 Why should sockets be used to mount integrated circuits?

Q2 What two things can damage integrated circuits?

When designing with ICs, you do not need to understand what is happening inside of them – it is usually too complicated. All you need to know is what the IC does and what the pin connections are. You can use them like building blocks, just connecting or joining them together to do a task. Some common ICs are the **741** which is an amplifier, the **555** which is a timer and a PIC which is a **programmable** chip. You choose the right one and can find how to use it from the manufacturer's information or from project books. You usually just copy the circuit and change the values of some of the components to make the circuit do what you want. Project books often provide a selection of circuits to get you started.

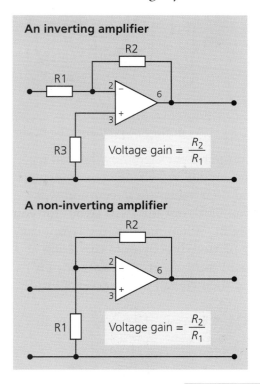

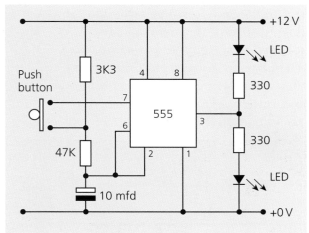

▲ *Fig 4* *555 circuit.*

Q3 Why do you think that ICs take small currents?

◄ *Fig 3* *741 circuits.*

Key words

555 – a timer chip
741 – an amplifier chip
chips – integrated circuits
ICs – integrated circuits
integrated circuits – small electronic circuits
programmable – a chip that can be loaded with a program and run
socket – allows ICs to be plugged in

SUMMARY

- Integrated circuits contain thousands of transistors in a very small space.
- They are made of semiconductor material.
- Always use sockets as ICs are sensitive to heat and can be damaged by soldering.
- Take care to connect the power supply to the chips the correct way around, as they are easily damaged.
- You need not know how they work, just what they do and their connections.

SUMMARY *activity*

Draw two different circuit diagrams using a 555 timer.

75 Printed circuit boards

In this section of the book you will learn the following things:
- why printed circuit boards are used;
- the methods used to make printed circuit boards;
- safety when using etching chemicals.

Printed circuit boards (PCBs) are made from a thin sheet of copper fixed to a glass fibre or resin paper base. The copper sheet is etched or milled away to leave the circuit connections. The legs of the components fit through holes drilled in the board and are soldered to the copper **pads** (Fig 1). The main advantages of PCBs are that they make very neat circuits possible and, once working correctly, can be easily reproduced.

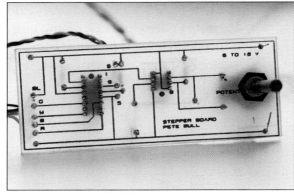

▲ *Fig 1* *A printed circuit board.*

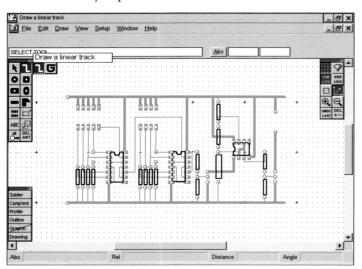

▲ *Fig 2* *PCB computer program.*

Computer packages now let you try out circuits and change components and their values on screen, and will even work out the PCB layout for you (Fig 2). When finished, the layout can be plotted directly onto the clean board using an **etch–resistant pen** and then etched using ferric chloride.

Q1 Why does the copper have to be clean?

Another method is to print onto acetate sheet for use with a photoresist board. This has to be exposed to ultraviolet light and then etched. Some systems use a small milling machine to cut out the copper sheet so avoiding the need for etching chemicals (Fig 3).

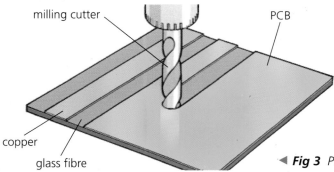

milling cutter

PCB

copper

glass fibre

◀ *Fig 3* *PCB milling machine.*

If you do not have a PCB program, then you can produce a layout by first using a prototyping board to build the circuit and arrange the components, and then drawing the positions and connecting them on tracing paper. Turning over the tracing paper will give you the PCB layout. This can be transferred to the board using an etch-resistant pen or **rub–down transfers** and then etched. When the board is etched, it can be cleaned using an abrasive rubber and then the holes will need to be drilled (Fig 4). The components are put on the fibre side of the board with their wires pushed through holes and soldered to the copper side. Any long leads are cut off close to the solder. Do not bend the leads over before soldering as this can make it difficult to change components in future.

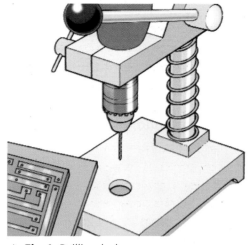
▲ **Fig 4** Drilling holes.

Safety

When etching, always use goggles, facemasks and aprons. Ferric chloride is corrosive.

Q2 Why are safety measures needed when using ferric chloride?

Q3 Why should you not bend over the leads of components before soldering?

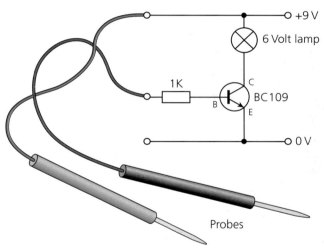
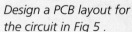

▲ **Fig 5** Simple tester circuit.

Key words

etch–resistant pen – a felt-tip pen whose ink resists etching fluid

pads – circular patches on the copper where components are soldered

PCB – printed circuit board

rub–down transfers – prepared, etch-resistant, component pads which can be rubbed on to the clean copper surface of a PCB

SUMMARY

- PCBs make producing neat, reliable circuits easy.
- They can be designed by computer, and printed, plotted or milled out. Once designed, any number can be produced.
- There are many different methods of producing PCBs ranging from using paper and pen through to using computer milling systems.
- Safety precautions must be taken when etching.

SUMMARY activity

Design a PCB layout for the circuit in Fig 5 .

76 Using electronic kits to make up circuits

In this section of the book you will learn the following things:
- why kits are used;
- the different types of kits;
- preventing damage when using kits.

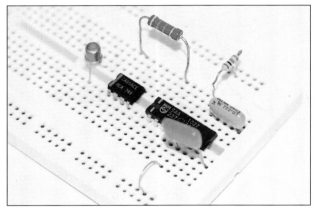

▲ **Fig 1** A breadboard.

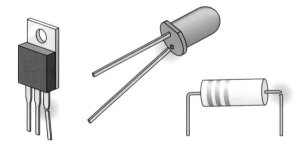

▲ **Fig 2** Component leads can break easily.

Kits can be used to build and test electronic circuits. Although you can use a computer program to do this, it is good for you to see and actually handle the parts.

Q1 Why do you use kits instead of a computer program to design circuits?

Kits are used to make it easy to try the **components** and to change them. The simplest is a **breadboard**, which lets you plug the components into a plastic board with small holes. Inside are connectors which make contact with the leads (Fig 1).

Electronic components usually have very thin leads. If you handle and bend them too many times, they can break off (Fig 2). Normally they are soldered together, but this can take a lot of time. Also, if you need to change the component it can be very difficult to do and it might be damaged. Components can be damaged by the heat of a soldering iron.

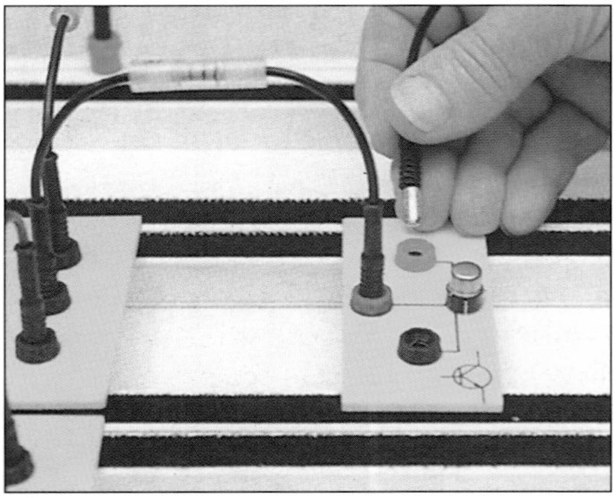

Some kits have the components fixed onto boards with connectors. Sometimes the component is showing, while on some others it is inside a small box (Fig 3). This prevents the leads to the components from being broken with use. Often the **circuit symbol** and name of the component is printed on the board, so that when you use them, you will learn and remember them. Some components connect together using wander plug leads, others plug into special boards.

◀ **Fig 3** Single components on kits.

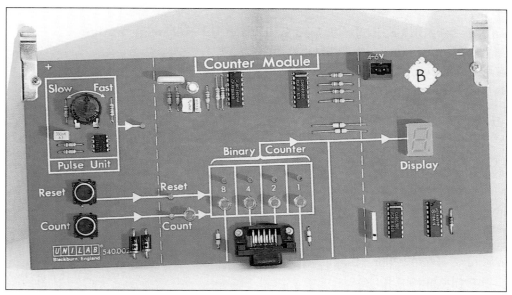

▲ **Fig 4** *A system board from a kit.*

Some kits, instead of having boards with one component on, use a systems approach (Fig 4). They have circuits split up into inputs, processes and outputs – each part being on a separate board. This lets you build more complicated circuits easily. You do not need to know how the circuit works, just what inputs, outputs and power it needs. The boards usually connect up only one way round so that mistakes are not easily made.

When using kits, make sure that you follow the makers' instructions so that you do not damage the components. Most components can be damaged by incorrect voltages, accidental shorts or being placed the wrong way around.

You usually use kits to test circuits before building them for use in your projects.

Q2 How are the components in kits protected from damage?

Q3 What must you do to prevent damage to the components in a kit?

Key words

breadboard – a board for building circuits on
circuit symbol – the drawing which represents the component in a circuit diagram
components – parts of a circuit

SUMMARY
- Kits are designed to make circuits easily and quickly.
- When using ordinary components too often, their leads may break so some kits protect individual components on small boards. Others take a systems approach and have a complete circuit on a board.

SUMMARY *activity*
Use small squares of card 20 mm x 50 mm. Draw components on each and use them as a kit to design a circuit.

77 Using microcontrollers

In this section of the book you will learn the following things:
- what microcontrollers are;
- how they are programmed;
- how microcontrollers can be used in your project work.

Microcontrollers are small computers on a single integrated circuit chip, known as **PICs** or Stamps. Many electronic devices in your home will have them fitted, such as the video recorder, microwave and washing machine (Fig 1). They make control projects a lot easier to design and make and use less components. They are designed to be programmed, then unplugged from the programming device and plugged into a project to make it work.

▲ *Fig 1* A microcontroller.

Q1 Why would TVs, washing machines and video recorders have microcontrollers in them?

Some microcontrollers can only be programmed once, so care must be taken to make sure your **program** is correct.

These are called OTP, which stands for one-time programming. The most useful is a flash (F) version, which can be put back into the **programmer**, and simply have a new program entered (Fig 2).

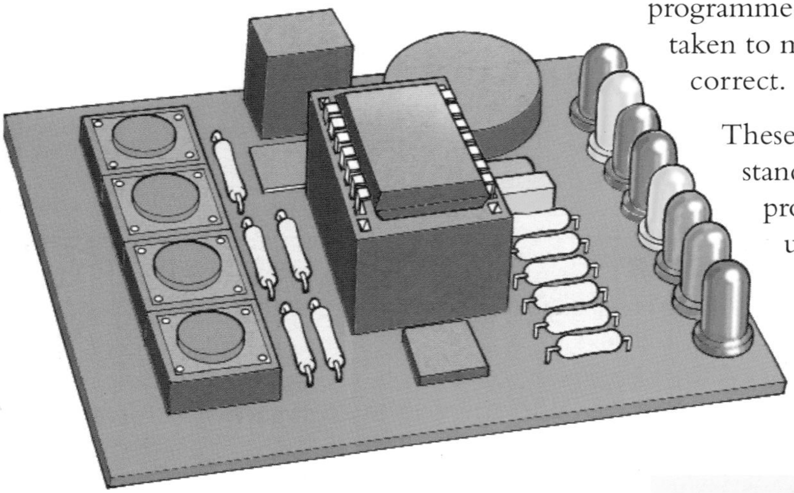

▲ *Fig 2* A programmer.

Q2 What do OTP and F mean?

Q3 What does the programmer do?

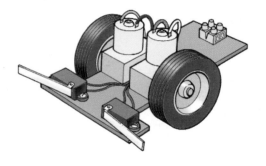

▲ **Fig 3** *Inputs on a project.*

There is a third type that has a small window through which it can be erased, using ultraviolet light. Some microcontrollers can accept analogue inputs and others, only digital ones.

If you have slowly changing input signals from light or temperature sensors, then you should choose a microcontroller with analogue inputs. You can compare the values of your inputs with numbers stored in memory – if they are bigger than those, then you can instruct the controller to do a task. If your inputs are on or off, i.e. from switches, then choose digital inputs (Fig 3).

Some programmers have a small liquid crystal display so that you can see your lines of program, others connect to a computer and let you test your programs on screen. There are special languages to control these devices – most are easy to use, but you will have to take some time to learn them. Some programs use a flow chart approach. Programs are usually quite short, but can be up to 100 lines long.

When you use the microcontroller, you will need a few extra components, a few resistors and switches for the inputs and transistor drivers if you want to control motors (Fig 4).

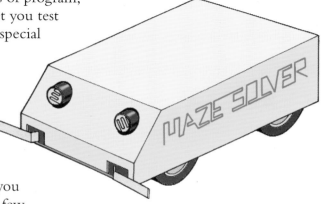

▲ **Fig 4** *A project using a microcontroller.*

Key words

microcontroller – a small programmable computer on a single chip

PIC – peripheral interface controller, the microcontroller

program – a list of computer instructions

programmer – a device which programs computer chips

SUMMARY

- A microcontroller is a small computer on a single chip. It can be plugged into a programmer and a program written into it.
- It can be plugged into a project and used to control the project. It accepts a range of inputs and can have up to eight outputs.
- If you want to drive motors, then you will need a few extra components.

SUMMARY activity

Design a simple project that could be controlled with a microcontroller which should have no more than two inputs and four outputs.

78 The use of computers in D&T

In this section of the book you will learn the following things:
- how to use computers to enhance your work;
- the range of software available for you to use;
- the reasons for using computers for your coursework.

Computers can be very useful in helping you to write about and produce drawings to describe how your project, or parts of it, will look. Some parts of the project could also be made or tested with the help of a computer. Remember that drawing on the computer can take a long time, so only use it if it is essential and there is no better way. The main advantage of using computers is that you can save your information to disk and work on it later. It is also easy to change things without completely retyping or redrawing. If you don't like your changes, then it is easy to go back to the original. There is a range of programs which help you do special tasks, such as designing textile patterns or electronic circuits. These make designing very much easier than using paper and pencil.

Computer-aided design (CAD)

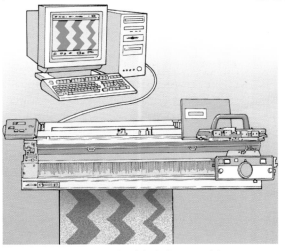

These are packages which let you draw and create ideas. You can produce drawings to show what your completed project will look like in three dimensions, or drawings to show the exact sizes and relationships of the parts of your project. More expensive **CAD** packages allow drawings to be rotated and stretched.

Computer-aided manufacture (CAM)

Using **CAM** packages, various machines can be plugged into the computer in order to machine, cut out, print, plot, sew, knit or mix the various materials to produce parts of your project (Fig 1).

▲ **Fig 1** A computerised knitting machine.

Computer-aided testing (CAT)

Computers can test designs to see if they work satisfactorily. You can use a spreadsheet program, such as *Excel*, to record changes to the ingredients in a recipe and to model these changes. Some **CAT** programs test structures without you having to build them. There are programs, such as *CrocClips*, which allow you to design electronic circuits on-screen and then to test if they work as you intended.

Word processors

You can write about your project using these. They enable you to produce neat text and lettering which can be cut out and pasted into your folio.

Control

These programs are used to **simulate** control projects. They allow various inputs to be connected to the computer, which is programmed to respond to them and produce some outputs. These outputs can then drive motors, lights and buzzers. Most programs have simple commands, such as 'switch on', 'switch off', 'wait', to allow you to tell the computer what to do (Fig 2).

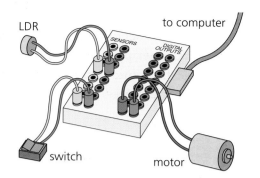

▲ **Fig 2** *A control box with motor, LDR and switch.*

Data handling

Spreadsheets and **databases** let you input a range of information or **data** about your project. This information can be linked together, searched and manipulated to produce component lists, cutting lists, price lists or nutritional value lists. Many manufacturers produce their information on disk so that you can search it for the details you need.

Simulation

You may see this word in National Curriculum information – it means using the computer to try out or test things. For example, you may put a list of prices of the ingredients of the food for a party into a spreadsheet. You can then simulate the total cost of the food for differing numbers of people or differing menus.

Internet browsers

These programs, such as *Netscape* and *Internet Explorer*, let you see and hear sites on the Internet. You can also download text, sounds and pictures to enhance your work. The Internet is a massive source of information about nearly everything. Using a **browser** you can search it to find information about your work or topic.

Q1 When could you use computers in your project work?

Q2 Give an example of when you could use a spreadsheet.

Q3 What are the advantages of using computers?

Key words

browser – a program which allows you to access the internet

CAD – computer-aided design

CAM – computer-aided manufacture

CAT – computer-aided testing

data – any information which is in a spreadsheet or database

database – a program which links together information which can then be searched

simulate – use the computer to try out something before actually making it

spreadsheet – a program which holds data in columns and rows, and allows changing one piece of data to have an effect on all the others

SUMMARY

- Using computers can help you to test, record, draw and make parts of your project work.
- You must decide when it is appropriate to use computers and when not to.
- There are programs which do specialised jobs such as control, electronic circuit and printed circuit design and textile pattern design.
- The Internet can be a source of information for your work.

SUMMARY activity

Using any drawing or paint package, draw a series of different coloured blocks which look as though they are disappearing into the distance.

79 Use of pneumatics

In this section of the book you will learn the following things:
- what pneumatics do;
- how pneumatics are used;
- the safety rules needed when using pneumatics.

Controlling movement

Pneumatics uses compressed air to produce movement. It uses **compressors**, **cylinders**, **valves** and tubes to transfer air around a system. It is capable of producing lots of power and sometimes is linked to electronics. You will have heard pneumatics in action, even if you have not actually seen it. When you hear the hissing of a lorry's brakes or the hissing of tube train doors; these are operated by pneumatics. It is used because it is powerful and needs low maintenance, especially in dirty and dusty places. You will see **hydraulics** used on bulldozers and diggers on building sites – this is similar to pneumatics, but a fluid is compressed instead of air (Fig 1).

▲ **Fig 1** Hydraulics in action.

Q1 What is the difference between pneumatics and hydraulics?

Pneumatic circuits are drawn like electronic circuits but with their own set of symbols. In school, most pneumatics work is done using kits that have quick release connectors and tubing which help you build circuits quickly (Fig 2). These kits that have the valves and pistons made from a clear plastic which allows you to see what is going on. Valves and pistons are very special components which can be used to make systems, but tend to be expensive and therefore cannot be permanently fitted to your projects.

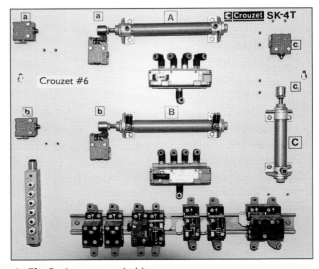

▲ **Fig 2** A pneumatic kit.

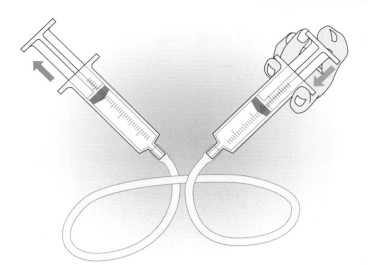

▲ **Fig 3** Using syringes.

One way around this, for relatively simple set-ups, is to use syringes and polythene tubing (Fig 3). Electric compressors are used to provide the compressed air, but simple systems can be run using a pumped up car inner tube (Fig 4).

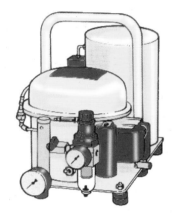

▶ **Fig 4** A compressor.

Safety

Compressed air must be used with care and there are some rules which must be followed:

1. Wear eye protection to prevent dust from being blown in your eyes.
2. Switch off the air supply before changing anything in the system.
3. Never let compressed air touch your skin, as it can force oil and particles under your skin.
4. Keep the pressure low – between one and two bar.

Q2 Why should you never let compressed air touch your skin?

Q3 What pressure should you use when making pneumatic models?

Key words

compressor – an electric pump which provides air under pressure

cylinder – converts air pressure into linear movement

hydraulics – using compressed fluid, usually a special oil, to move things

pneumatics – using compressed air to move things

valve – controls the distribution of air in a system

SUMMARY

■ Pneumatics is using compressed air to push pistons in and out of cylinders; the air is controlled by valves.

■ It can produce lots of power and is one reason why it is sometimes used instead of electronics.

SUMMARY
activity

Connect two syringes together with plastic tube. Make sure that one piston is out as far as it can be and the other is fully in. Press down the one which is out and feel the pressure exerted by the other. Now completely fill the syringes and tube with water and repeat the test. What is the difference?

80 Pneumatic cylinders

In this section of the book you will learn the following things:
- what cylinders do;
- how single- and double-acting cylinders work;
- how to work out the forces involved.

▲ **Fig 1** A single-acting cylinder.

Pneumatic cylinders are like a bicycle pump, but in reverse. If you force air into the bicycle pump, its piston, the part which you pump up and down to fill your tyres, slides out. In a cylinder, this force would be quite strong and capable of operating a part of a project or machine. The movement, called the outstroke, is linear, i.e. in a straight line.

Q1 What is the moving part of a cylinder called?

The air in this case causes the piston to move out and it will stay there. A spring is used to return the piston to its original position. These cylinders are called **single-acting** cylinders (Fig 1).

If you need a power **stroke** for the piston both in and out then a **double-acting** cylinder is required. This has a **port** (inlet) both behind and in front of the piston (Fig 2). When the piston is out, air pressure is used to return it. This means that the cylinder can push and pull with equal force. The ends of the piston rod are often threaded so that different types of actuators can be fitted. These can be rollers, brackets and clevises for connecting to parts of a project.

You can use syringes for simple pneumatic and hydraulic set-ups, but you must remember that they will not produce the accuracy or forces of real pneumatic cylinders. They can be connected together using plastic tubing and fittings such as Y connectors, as used for fish tanks and aquariums (Fig 3).

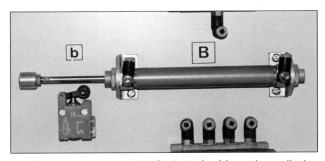

▲ **Fig 2** A double-acting cylinder.

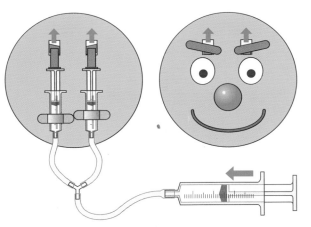

▲ **Fig 3** Using syringes for a simple project.

The force which a cylinder can produce is calculated as:

pressure × area = force

where the air pressure acting on the piston is in Newtons per square mm (N/mm²), the area of the piston in mm², and the force in Newtons (N) (Fig 4).

▶ *Fig 4* Forces.

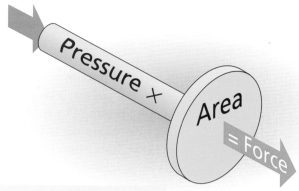

Q2 When would you need to use a double-acting cylinder?
Q3 If the air pressure to a cylinder is 0.1 N/mm² and the piston's area was 500 mm², what will be the force exerted by the piston?

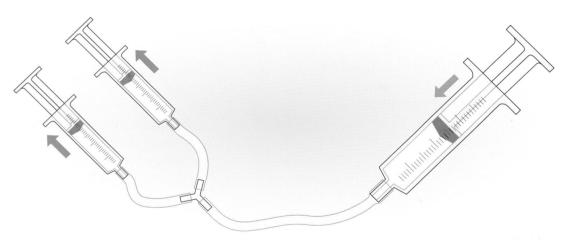

▲ *Fig 5* A large cylinder operating two small cylinders.

Key words

double-acting – air pressure pushes piston out and in
port – where the air enters or leaves a pneumatic component
single-acting – air pressure pushes piston out, a spring returns it
stroke – the movement of the piston

SUMMARY

- Cylinders are used to give movement from compressed air. They can be single-acting, the piston being returned by a spring, or double-acting, the piston being returned by air pressure.
- Simple systems can be made using syringes.
- Cylinders can have attachments such as rollers fitted.

SUMMARY activity

Connect a large syringe to two smaller ones using a Y connector and tubing (Fig 5). What effect does the large syringe have on the two small ones when pressed?

81 Valves

In this section of the book you will learn the following things:
- what valves do in pneumatic circuits;
- what the ports do;
- how pneumatic valves are used in circuits.

Valves control the air in a pneumatic system – they are the equivalent of switches in an electronic circuit. The **ports** are where the compressed air is fed into and out of a component. The port where the air comes out of the valve is called the **exhaust**. Valves are described by the number of ports they have, i.e. two, three and five port valves. They may be **operated** by several different methods, including push buttons, keys, solenoids, plungers and foot pedals. These are shown on the

Q1 How can valves be operated?

symbols of the valves. The symbol for the valve shows it both on and off as two blocks one above the other (Fig 1). As with electronic circuits, the symbol shows the connections for the valve, and not its size. In Fig 2, port 1 is the air in, port 2 is the air to the cylinder, and port 3 is the exhaust. The air going into port 1 is blocked, but the exhaust is open having allowed the closing cylinder to release air by the exhaust. In Fig 3, the button is pressed, port 1 is connected to port 2 and air goes to the cylinder making it **stroke**. The exhaust is blocked. When the button is released, the valve goes back to where it was in Fig 2, the air from port 1 is blocked and the cylinder's spring pushes the plunger back, exhausting to port 3.

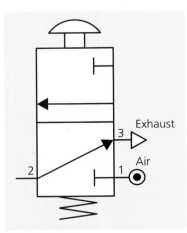

▲ **Fig 1** The symbol for a button operated 3 port valve.

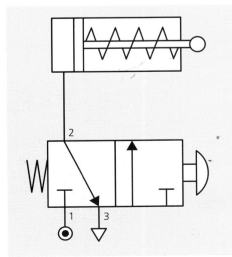

▲ **Fig 2** A button operated 3 port valve with cylinder.

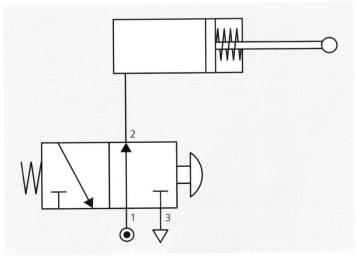

▲ **Fig 3** The valve with the button pressed, the cylinder operates.

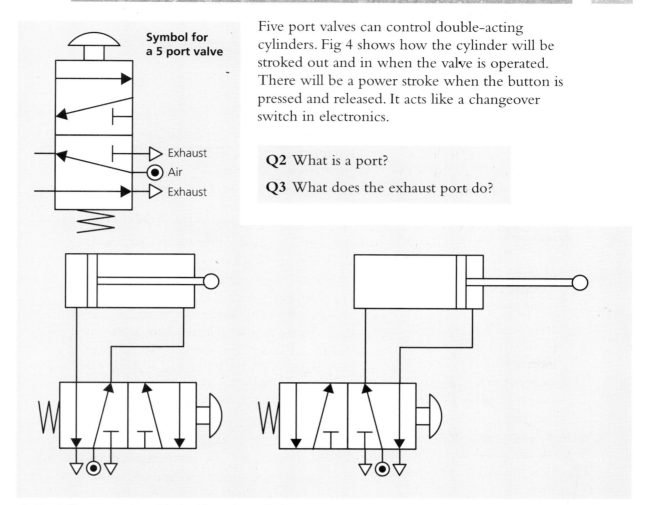

Symbol for a 5 port valve

Five port valves can control double-acting cylinders. Fig 4 shows how the cylinder will be stroked out and in when the valve is operated. There will be a power stroke when the button is pressed and released. It acts like a changeover switch in electronics.

Q2 What is a port?

Q3 What does the exhaust port do?

▲ **Fig 4** *Five port valve with double-acting cylinder.*

You will find a list of pneumatic symbols on page 212. These can be photocopied then cut and pasted to make up pneumatic diagrams easily.

Key words

exhaust – the port where air leaves the system

operator – the method in which the valve is operated, e.g. push button, lever, etc.

port – where air enters and leaves a pneumatic component

stroke – the movement of the piston in a cylinder

SUMMARY

- Valves act like switches in electronic circuits. They can be on, off or changeover.
- They control the flow of air around the system.
- They are named by the number of ports they have.
- They can be operated in a number of ways, e.g. lever, roller, pushbutton or solenoid.

SUMMARY activity

Draw the circuit in Fig 4 in both on and off states and colour in the air and exhaust lines to show what is happening.

82 Regulators and reservoirs

In this section of the book you will learn the following things:
- why restrictors, regulators and reservoirs are used;
- how to slow down the operation of cylinders;
- how reservoirs are used to make time delays.

When a valve is operated, the piston in a cylinder moves quickly. Sometimes, you will want to slow down this operation or to delay it. We can use a range of components called **regulators**, **restrictors** and **reservoirs** (Fig 1).

Q1 Why do we need to slow down the speed of operation of cylinders?

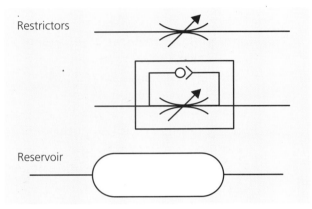

▲ **Fig 1** Symbols for regulator, restrictor and reservoir.

Unidirectional flow regulators or restrictors allow a free flow of air in one direction, but a restricted flow in the other. They have a small ball held against a seat by a spring. When air flows in one direction, it overcomes the spring pressure and lifts the ball off the seat. The air then flows depending on how the regulating screw is set. In the other direction, the air pressure just pushes the ball more firmly on the seat and no airflow takes place (Fig 2).

Q2 How does a unidirectional restrictor stop air flowing in one direction?

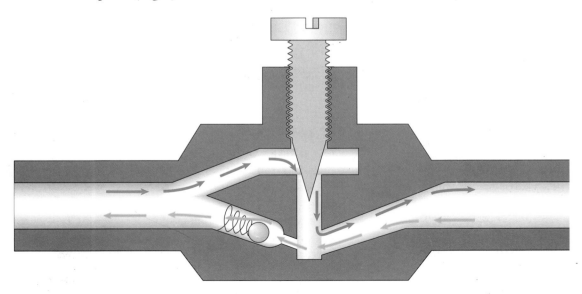

▲ **Fig 2** Cross-section of a unidirectional regulator.

Bi-directional restrictors reduce the flow of air in both directions. Both types of regulator have a screw which restricts the flow of air to a certain level – unscrewing it allows more air through, screwing it up reduces the air supply.

On page 158, we said that pneumatics were used to control sliding doors. It could be very dangerous if doors opened and closed too rapidly. Restrictors are used to slow down the action of cylinders. If you put your finger over a cycle pump connector, it is difficult to push the handle down. It will only move if you let air leak past your finger, this is what a regulator does. Instead of the cylinder being able to exhaust freely, it is restricted and only a limited flow of air occurs. The cylinder closes slowly (Fig 3).

The reservoir is a container for air. If you want to delay a valve or cylinder operating, you arrange for the air to go through a restrictor and fill up the reservoir. When the reservoir is full, pressure then builds up to operate the valve or cylinder. The time taken to fill the reservoir is the delay (Fig 4).

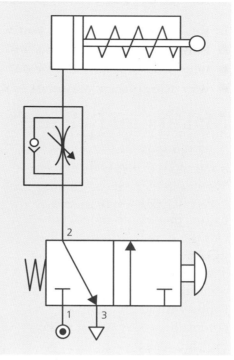

▲ **Fig 3** Speed control of a cylinder.

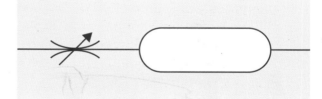

▲ **Fig 4** Time delay using a reservoir.

Q3 What electronic component is similar in action to a reservoir?

Key words

bi-directional – flow in both directions
regulator – controls the maximum pressure to part of a system
reservoir – used to create a time delay
restrictor – controls the flow of air in a pipe line
unidirectional – flow in one direction only

SUMMARY

- Cylinders can operate at high speeds – they may need to be slowed down by restricting the exhaust.
- Restrictors can be unidirectional or bi-directional.
- Reservoirs take time to fill with air and delay the opening of valves or cylinders.

SUMMARY activity

Make a model of a unidirectional restrictor from card and clear plastic sheet to show how the spring loaded ball works.

83 Commercial products

In this section of the book you will learn the following things:
- how commercial products are designed and made;
- why prototypes, modifications and new models are needed;
- why asking users and market research is important.

Makers and clients

A product can be developed for a client in a number of ways. The client could go straight to the **designer** or maker and ask them to make something. They would discuss exactly what was needed and the price. If the designer or maker had made something similar before, they could modify an existing design. Otherwise they would start from the beginning. This product would be a one-off. If the **customer** were not happy with it, they could complain directly to the maker.

Q1 How does a designer know what a client wants?

▲ *Fig 1* The simplest product cycle.

Designers and clients

Sometimes the client might go to a designer first and explain what they want. The designer will make drawings and then find a manufacturer. They will return to the client to check on the suitability of the design before telling the maker to continue.

▲ *Fig 2* Testing the product.

In a larger situation the client may be a company that employs designers and staff to make the product which will be sold in bulk. They will do market research to identify needs and produce **prototypes** which will be tested (Fig 2). They might be tested by people using them for a time. Any faults or unsatisfactory elements will then be modified until an acceptable design is found. It will then be put into production and sold.

This design cycle could be quite short for simple goods, but may take a long time for complex devices like buildings and cars. In the case of food products, tastings will be undertaken to see if the design is satisfactory. Some completely new products will be designed after finding out if there is a need by using market research. When products already exist, new models will be brought out based on user comments or **market research**. The selling price is more than the cost of design, manufacture and distribution so that products usually make a profit. When making your projects, it is important to let others test it and give their comments.

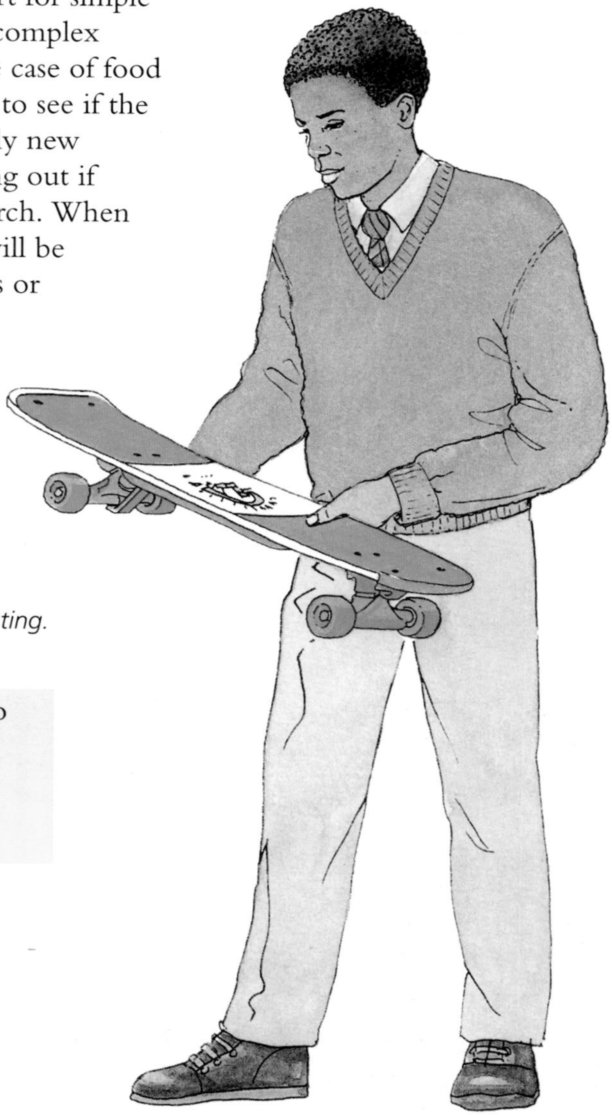

▶ *Fig 3* *Toy testing.*

Q2 How are improvements made to existing products?

Q3 How can designers find out if a new product is likely to sell?

Key words

customer – the person who buys the product

designer – the person who devises what the product will be like

market research – finding out what people need or want

prototype – a model to test an idea before production

SUMMARY

- Product cycles vary depending upon how many people are involved. The simplest is between customer and designer/maker.
- Large companies have complex product cycles.
- Market research helps manufacturers improve existing products or test new ideas.
- Commercial products are designed to make a profit.

SUMMARY activity

The manufacturer of Action Men or Barbie Doll type toys are trying to price their products. What costs might they take into account other than the costs of the raw materials?

84 Investigating products

In this section of the book you will learn the following things:

■ how to investigate commercial products;

■ the type of questions you will need to ask;

■ different cultures may solve design problems in different ways.

When looking at commercial products we can usually say quickly whether we like them, based on how they look, i.e. first impressions. This is obviously important, but after using the product for some time, you might begin to notice things which are not so good.

As you become experienced, it will help you make sensible decisions when you are buying goods for yourself.

Q1 Why do we need to investigate commercial products?

What are the ingredients?

What are the components?

▲ **Fig 1** Questions you could ask.

When investigating products in school, you will not have a lot of time to find out these things, so you need to speed up your investigation. You could make up a series of charts, with points to check. Obviously, food or textiles may need a different set of questions or points to electrical products (Fig 2). You should ask:

Product	A steam iron
Questions about the product	My answers
What scientific principles are involved?	Heating using electricity passed through a resistance element. A bimetal strip controls the temperature. Water is changed into steam.
What are the mechanisms?	There are cams in the thermostat. Flexible connectors for the lead. Valves control the water.
How is it powered?	By electricity.
What materials have been used?	Plastics for the body. Copper for the electrical conductors. Aluminium for the sole plate.
Why have they been used?	Plastics for easy clean and electrical safety. Aluminium for lightness. Copper for low resistance.

▲ **Fig 2** Questions about the product.

What scientific principles are used in the product?

Does the product rely on mechanisms, electricity, structure, form or properties of ingredients for its main purpose?

If so, what do they do and how do they do it?

Why were the materials or **ingredients** chosen?

What **characteristics** do they have?

What **processes** do you think were used to produce the various parts?

If several materials, ingredients or processes are combined to make the product, how do they link or **interact** together?

Do you think that it is a good or a bad design? How will you judge good or bad design?

Is the product pleasant to feel, hold, look at, wear or taste? What makes it pleasant?

It is often a good idea to compare similar products from several manufacturers because you can focus on the reasons for the different aspects of the designs (Fig 3). Different cultures also may have different ways of solving the same design problems, so they may give you some new ideas. They may have other materials or methods of manufacture they can use. The use of materials or ingredients in food may depend on religious beliefs. If you can, investigate these.

▲ **Fig 3** Similar products from different manufacturers.

▲ **Fig 4** Foods from different cultures.

Q2 How do the ingredients of a salad interact?

Q3 Why is it good to look at designs from different cultures?

Key words

characteristics – the properties something has

ingredients – the individual parts of a recipe of food

interaction – how things work together

processes – how the materials are made or manipulated

SUMMARY

■ *Investigation of commercial products helps you to become more discerning.*

■ *You are trying to find out why the manufacturer uses certain methods and materials.*

■ *Comparing different products shows that there is always a range of answers to any design problem.*

SUMMARY activity

Cut out four advertisements for computer systems from different producers. Compare the differences in price and specification in a simple chart. Try to decide which one would be the best buy.

85 Product analysis

In this section of the book you will learn the following things:
- the reasons for taking products to pieces;
- how to disassemble products in a logical way;
- whether the packaging describes the product accurately.

When investigating **commercial** products, try to discover how they are made, just by looking at them first. With some products, this would be easy to do. With others, it might be necessary to take them apart, or **dissassemble** them, so that you can find out how they are constructed. You are looking to see how the various parts fit together and how parts rotate or link together if they have mechanisms. When you start, you must **record** the order that you take things apart.

This could be drawn using dotted lines to show where things link together (Fig 1). The parts may be made of different materials, so you need to find out why particular materials are used. Try to identify the important characteristics of the materials so you can understand the reasons why they were chosen by the manufacturer.

Q1 Why do you need to record how a product comes apart?

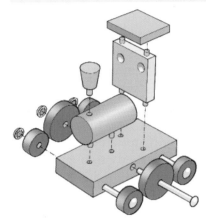

▲ **Fig 1** *Recording how the product is made.*

Q2 What reason would there be for using plastic gears in a toy?

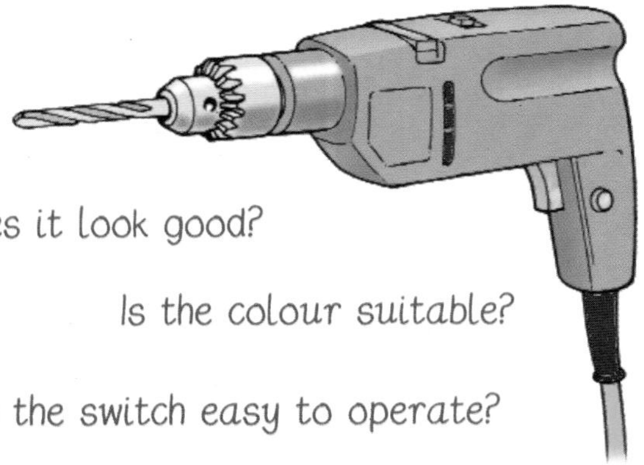

How is it to hold?

Is it comfortable?

Does it look good?

Is the colour suitable?

Is the switch easy to operate?

▲ **Fig 2** *Aesthetics – how things look.*

How the product looks is important. Is it well designed for its use? Is its shape good to hold? Is the colour scheme right? (Fig 2) You can look at some foods in the same way, e.g. breakfast foods like cornflakes, or muesli which is made up of loose mixtures of flakes, nuts and seeds. These could be split up into groups and weighed, and the weights converted into percentages of the total weight.

▲ **Fig 3** *Analysis of the ingredients.*

The nutritional values for the different parts could be calculated (Fig 3). You could suggest why the different ingredients are used, how much they cost, and how you think you could improve the product. Some parts or ingredients are used because they look good, and have little to do with how the product performs.

The **packaging** is also a major part of product **analysis**. What does it say on the packaging? Does it describe the product well? Is it truthful and accurate in its claims? (Fig 4).

▲ **Fig 4** *Accurate packaging claims – do manufacturers always tell the truth?*

Q3 Why is the picture on the packet often slightly different from the actual product inside?

Key words

analysis – finding out
commercial – things that are bought and sold
disassembly – taking things to pieces
packaging – the containers in which products are sold
record – write down, photograph or draw

SUMMARY

■ Product analysis is finding out how a product is designed and put together.
■ It is important to know why certain materials were used.
■ If mechanisms are used, how do they operate?
■ Food, in some cases, can be broken down into its basic ingredients. Calculations can be done to find nutritional values.

SUMMARY *activity*

Take to pieces a product such as a biro or a small torch and draw a diagram of how the parts fit together.

86 Healthy eating

In this section of the book you will learn the following things:

- why it is necessary to eat healthily;
- the good things to eat;
- the things to be careful about eating.

Keeping healthy

We need to eat food and enjoy it for several reasons:

- Growth – to help us when growing to produce strong bones and teeth.
- Energy – to help us to play, work and exercise.
- Health – to keep our bodies working well, and help us to recover from illness quickly.

We need to eat a balanced diet – one which contains a range of different foods. To stay healthy we should generally eat more fruit, vegetables and **fibre** (Fig 1), and less **fats** and **sugars**. Where foods contain fats, e.g. milk and dairy foods, we should try to use lower fat versions. If we do not have some of these foods we may become ill.

Q1 Why is healthy eating important?

There are statutory dietary **guidelines** which we should try to follow when developing recipes and meals.

▲ **Fig 1** Healthy foods – fruit and vegetables.

Some **ingredients** can have a harmful effect on our bodies if too much is eaten (Fig 2):

- Too much sugar can cause increases in weight and tooth decay.
- Too much fat can cause increases in weight and can lead to heart disease.
- Too much salt may give you high blood pressure.
- Too many energy foods, such as chocolate and sweets, can make you overweight.
- Not enough fibre can cause problems with the digestive system.

▲ **Fig 2** Unhealthy foods if eaten in excess.

Many prepared meals available in supermarkets and fast food outlets contain too much sugar, salt and fat. Several supermarkets are now concentrating on making these foods in 'Healthy Eating' versions and on improving their nutritional values (Fig 3).

▲ **Fig 3** *'Healthy eating' symbols from packaging.*

We can tell the ingredients of packaged food by reading the label. It is difficult to make decisions because you would have to look at everything you eat and add up the amounts of sugar, fat and salt, as well as other ingredients. The secret is to try to eat a balanced diet.

Q2 What are the statutory guidelines?

Q3 What can happen if you do not follow these rules?

Key words

fat – part of meat and dairy products

fibre – part of fruit, vegetables, pulses

guidelines – helpful information

ingredients – the individual parts of a recipe or food

sugars – used as sweeteners

SUMMARY

■ It is important to eat a balanced diet. This means eating a range of different foods.

■ Try to avoid eating too many fats, sugars and salt in your food.

■ These often occur in prepared foods. It is not easy to find out what you are eating.

SUMMARY *activity*

Look at three different 'Healthy Eating' packaged foods and try to find out from the packaging what the producers claim is the healthy aspect of the foods.

87 Foods and nutrition

In this section of the book you will learn the following things:
- the nutrients that foods contain;
- what these nutrients are;
- what nutrients do for us.

Balanced diets

The food we eat provides us with the **nutrients** we need to live. A **balanced diet** should provide us with all the nutrients we need. These nutrients can be divided into three main groups:

- Nutrients which help us grow – **proteins**.
- Nutrients which help to give us energy – **carbohydrates**.
- Nutrients which help to keep us healthy – **vitamins** and **minerals**.

> **Q1** Which nutrients keep us healthy?

Those which help us to grow and repair any injuries are called proteins. They are found in meat, fish, eggs, cheese, milk and **pulses** (Fig 1).

Those that give us energy are called carbohydrates. They are found in all starches and sugars. Starches are in bread, pasta, rice, potatoes and breakfast cereals (Fig 2). Too many carbohydrates will be stored by the body as fat.

Sugars are found naturally in fruit and milk and there are also refined sugars which are added to food and drinks (Fig 3).

Fats give us energy, but too much fat in our diet can cause us to put on weight. There are two types of fats, saturated and unsaturated fats. Saturated fat is generally not good for your health as it can cause high blood pressure. These fats are found in meat, milk, cheese and butter. Unsaturated fats are found in oils and low fat spreads and are better for you. Fats do contain vitamins needed for good health, however (Fig 4).

▲ **Fig 1** Sources of proteins.

▲ **Fig 2** Sources of carbohydrates.

▲ **Fig 3** *Sources of sugars.*

▲ **Fig 4** *Sources of fats.*

The nutrients which keep us healthy are vitamins and minerals. These are mainly found in fruit and vegetables and are needed in very small amounts but are essential to keep us healthy.

Calcium is a mineral needed for strong bones and teeth, and iron is essential for healthy blood and circulation.

Fibres are necessary and come from plant materials. They help in the digestion of your food and can help prevent some bowel diseases.

Most foods also contain small amounts of water, which help to replace water lost by sweating, excretion and breathing.

The amounts of all these nutrients contained in a food can be found on the labels on food packaging.

Q2 Why do some athletes eat pasta before a long marathon?

Q3 How does the fibre content of some foods help our bodies?

Key words

balanced diet – a diet giving all or most of the nutrients needed
carbohydrates – sugars and starches
minerals – found in vegetables and fruit, keeps you healthy
nutrient – ingredients which are beneficial to life
protein – body building material
pulses – a general word for beans, peas and lentils
vitamins – found in vegetables and fruit, keep you healthy

SUMMARY

■ Foods contain the nutrients needed for life. You should get all the nutrients you need from what you eat each day.
■ Carbohydrates and fats provide energy.
■ Vitamins and minerals are needed by our bodies in small amounts.

SUMMARY activity

Make a chart of the foods that you have eaten today under the headings: Proteins, Carbohydrates, Fats, Vitamins, Minerals. Tick off what each food contributes to your diet.

88 The labelling of food products

In this section of the book you will learn the following things:
- what labels will tell you about the product;
- why we need to know this information;
- how we can use the information provided.

Labelling

The label on its packaging gives you a lot of information about the product. It is useful to help you to compare it with other similar products and make decisions about value for money, how healthy it is and if there are any **ingredients** which you may not like or are allergic to. **Vegetarians**, and some religious groups, do not eat meat or certain ingredients so they need to know what foods contain (Fig 1).

> **Q1** Give three reasons why you might need to know the ingredients of a product.

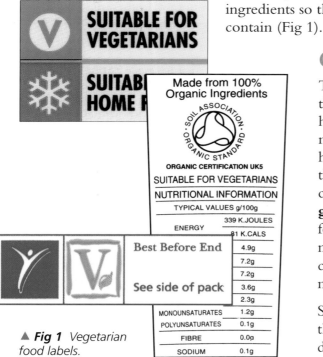

▲ **Fig 1** Vegetarian food labels.

Choices

The label may include relatively simple things like how to prepare the product and how long to keep it, right through to nutritional values. As people become more health conscious, then the more important the information becomes. A recent health concern has been about the use of **genetically modified** ingredients in food. Pressure from consumers has led to most manufacturers stating if their foods contain these ingredients. This lets you make a choice about what you eat.

Sometimes producers make claims about their products, e.g. that they are healthy, do not contain certain ingredients or are fat free.

Information from labels

Most labels will contain:
- The name of the product.
- What it is made from – a list of ingredients. These are usually put in order of weight, with the heaviest ingredients first.
- The 'use by', 'best before' or 'best before end' date. This tells you how long you can store the food before use.

- The 'display until' date tells the supermarket or shop how long they can keep the product on display (Fig 2).
- How the product must be stored, e.g. in fridge, freezer or cool, dry place.
- The place of origin – where the product comes from.
- The name and address of the manufacturer or supplier.
- How to use the product – the cooking or preparation instructions.
- The weight or volume of the product.

NUTRITION INFORMAT	
Energy	193 Kcal/803 kJ
Carbohydrate	4 g
BEST BEFORE END DEC. 1996	

11∕00
LOT: 06 0

PRODUCE OF
SPAIN
SELL BY:
03 MAR
ENJOY BY:
05 MAR
089

Best before end
FEB 00
B8246E

BEST BEFORE END
MAR 00 9070
STORE IN A COOL DRY PLACE

▲ **Fig 2** 'Use by' food labels.

Accuracy

The description of the ingredients must be accurate. If it says on the label 'milk chocolate covered ice cream', then the product must contain real chocolate and real cream. Often, 'choc ice' means there is no real chocolate or cream in the product. It will probably say containing 'milk solids' and 'cocoa flavoured coating' (Fig 3).

Q2 Why does the supermarket need to know the 'display until date'?

Q3 Why is labelling important for frozen foods?

Daisyfresh Stores **20 CHOC ICES**

VANILLA FLAVOUR ICE CREAM COVERED WITH CHOCOLATE FLAVOUR COATING

INGREDIENTS

Partially Reconstituted Whey Protein, Chocolate Flavour Coating (25%) [contains: Coconut Oil, Sugar, Whey Powder, Fat Reduced Cocoa Powder, Emulsifier], Sugar, Hydrogenated Vegetable Fat, Whey Powder, Emulsifier (E471), Stabilisers (Guar Gum, Sodium Alginate), Flavouring, Colours (Curcumin Annato)

Regal

Delicious layers of chocolate sponge and chocolate cream topped with a rich chocolate sauce

Chocolate Gateau

Keep Frozen

▲ **Fig 3** Real or non-real ingredients.

Key words

genetically modified – food which has its genes altered

ingredients – the parts making up a product

vegetarians – people who do not eat animal products

SUMMARY

- Labelling tells you a range of information about the product.
- It includes nutritional details. It gives storage and has 'how to use' information.
- It will have dates by which the food has to be used.

SUMMARY activity

Get five labels from food products. Write down the types of information on the labels, e.g. nutritional, ingredients, health claims. Do the labels all contain similar information?

89 Food ingredients and their uses

In this section of the book you will learn the following things:
- what effect a range of ingredients has;
- why various ingredients are used;
- what is used to preserve fruits and vegetables.

You will need to know what effect a range of ingredients has when developing new recipes. This will help you know what the product or recipe will look or taste like when it is finished. Adding ingredients can have different effects. Each ingredient will add to the taste or look of the food. Some will make a very small, almost undetectable, change to the **flavour**. Others may totally change the look of the product and have a major effect.

Q1 Why do you need to know the effects of adding various ingredients to a recipe?

▲ *Fig 1* Flour, bread and cakes.

The purpose of using flour in a product is to provide **bulk** and to help thicken liquids like soups. It also adds carbohydrates and flavour (Fig 1).

Fat adds flavour, acts as a shortening agent in pastry, holds air in cake mixes and adds moisture.

Sugar adds or changes flavour and is used to **sweeten** recipes. It is also a bulking agent, it gives nutritional value, and makes pastry light. It also provides us with a source of energy. It is used to **preserve** fruit – jam is fruits preserved in sugar (Fig 2).

▼ *Fig 2* Jams and preserves.

Egg is used to bind ingredients together. It acts like a gluey substance and helps to hold air in meringues and can be used to set food, and to coat and **glaze** it. It is also nutritious.

Q2 Give three different reasons for using sugar in a recipe.

Both salt and vinegar are used for pickling. Meat, fruit and vegetables can be stored by putting them into salt or vinegar. Pickles are a good example of this (Fig 3).

Natural or artificial food colourings are available to change the colour of food products. You will often see them used in children's party food, such as cakes and icing (Fig 4).

▲ *Fig 3* Pickled vegetables.

Spices and herbs are used to flavour foods, including cakes, curries and soups. Spices are ground up seeds, bark, roots or the pods of various plants. Herbs are the leaves of plants which can be used whole or cut up.

◀ *Fig 4* Colour used in celebration cakes.

Q3 How can you preserve fruit or vegetables?

Key words

bulking – providing mass or volume

flavour – the taste of a product

glazing – putting a shiny surface on pastry

preserve – to keep fruit or vegetables from spoiling

sweeten – add sugar to make taste less sharp

SUMMARY

■ Each ingredient can be used for a variety of reasons.

■ To make up or modify recipes, you need to know what each one does. Some alter the flavour, some the texture. Some can have a big impact on some aspect of the recipe, for example, too much chilli in a curry!!!

SUMMARY *activity*

Look at recipes for scones, quiche and strawberry meringue. Write down the main ingredients of each recipe and say why they are used.

90 Altering foods to suit us

In this section of the book you will learn the following things:
- why foods are changed or modified;
- the food requirements of different people;
- changing recipes to take advantage of availability.

When developing recipes or new products, there are many reasons to change them.

Some products will need to be changed to make them:

- More healthy – for example, to add more fibre and to reduce the fat content. In Western diets we generally eat too little fibre in our foods and this can lead to various digestive problems.

it's 98% fat free

it's a great source of bran fibre

it's made from just one ingredient

it has no added salt or sugar

A Great Source of fibre

HIGH IN FIBRE

▲ **Fig 1** *We need more fibre in our foods.*

Q1 Breakfast cereals often have ingredients added to them to make them more healthy, name two things. These are often advertised on the packet.

- Suitable for special diets – some people do not eat meat or meats such as pork because of their religion. Sometimes meat has to be prepared in a special way before they can eat it.

▲ **Fig 2** *Foods suitable for vegetarians and vegans.*

Vegetarians and **vegans** do not eat animal products, so recipes have to exclude any products, such as fats, gelatine or rennet (used in cheese making), which have come from animals (Fig 2). There are people who need specially prepared products because they have an illness or condition which can be affected by what they eat. Some foods need to be gluten free for this reason. Babies, when they start eating solid foods, are often fed products designed specifically for their needs.

▲ **Fig 3** *Some drinks have too much sugar.*

■ Taste differently – for instance, to make products less sweet. We all know that very sweet things lead to tooth decay, so producers might try to make their fruit drinks less sweet, particularly those which are **targeted** at children (Fig 3). Foods may need to be made more, or less, spicy to suit different tastes. Think about the taste of some prepared curries – some people like them very hot, while others want a much more delicate flavour.

Sometimes a product is changed to keep it within the national dietary guidelines or to improve its keeping or storage characteristics.

Some ingredients may be available at certain times of the year – for instance, there may be lots of strawberries. A recipe using another fruit can be changed to take advantage of a cheaper **alternative** (Fig 4).

▲ **Fig 4** *Availability of produce.*

Q2 What ingredients could you add to a curry to make it hotter?

Q3 What sweeteners are used in drinks? Look at some labels to find out.

Key words

alternative – another type of ingredient
targeted – advertised or sold for a particular group
vegan – someone who does not eat any animal products

SUMMARY

■ Foods can be changed to suit the users' needs.
■ They may need to be changed for health or religious reasons.
■ The taste can be modified to make the recipe more acceptable to certain groups.
■ Availability of ingredients may cause changes to be made.

SUMMARY activity

Modify a lasagna recipe to make it acceptable for a vegetarian. Write down a list of ingredients and say which ones would have to be changed and why.

91 Which product tastes the best?

In this section of the book you will learn the following things:
- why you need to taste test food products;
- how the tasting is to be done;
- what you are trying to find out about the samples.

◀ **Fig 1** Foods for testing.

Testing samples

It is very important to **taste** and **test** food products. You will need to develop your skills in this area in order to modify, change or select ingredients, and to make decisions about the products you are trying out or testing (Fig 1). You should get used to making up lists of words that describe the various characteristics of the **sample**. For example, words to describe an orange may be: sweet, sour, bitter, sharp, soft, dry, juicy. A **star profile** can be made up using these words (Fig 2).

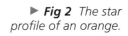

▶ **Fig 2** The star profile of an orange.

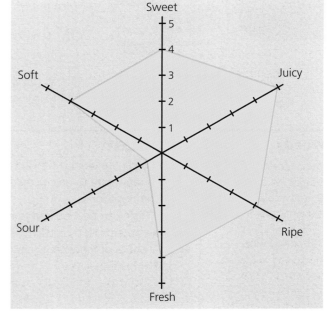

Q1 What four words could you use to describe a hamburger?

Blind tasting is where the samples are hidden from view so that you compare them just on their taste. You could use a blindfold so that the tasters do not know what they are tasting (Fig 3). Tasting can be done in a **booth** so that the tasters cannot talk to or see each other. Sometimes the tasting will be done using low, coloured lighting that changes the apparent colour of the food so that the products cannot be easily recognised. The samples should be given numbers, letters or symbols so that they can be identified later (Fig 4). You might have to say which sample you like best, or to compare the flavour or texture of several samples.

▲ **Fig 3** Blind tasting.

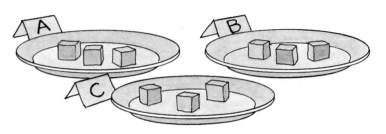

▲ **Fig 4** Identifying samples.

Q2 Why is tasting sometimes done in booths?

Q3 Why should the samples be given numbers, letters or symbols instead of words?

When setting up tests, the first thing to do is to decide why you are testing and what you are trying to find out. It could be to find the taste that most people like best, or the saltiest food sample. The next step is to decide how you are going to set up the test and how the tests will be done so that the results will be reliable. You might find this quite a difficult task. When you have people trying samples, hygiene is very important so you should use disposable knives, forks and spoons.

Key words

booth – partitions which prevent people seeing each other
sample – a small amount of food or drink for tasting
star profile – a diagram to show a food's characteristics
tasting – eating or drinking to find out the texture or taste of food or drink
testing – trying out things

SUMMARY

■ Testing foods by tasting allows you to try out new or changed recipes.
■ Blind tasting is testing purely by taste or texture, without being influenced by seeing the food.
■ You should set up your tests to make sure that they are reliable.

SUMMARY
activity

Prepare three different types of mushroom soup, e.g. tinned, packet and fresh. Place each in a bowl, making sure that you know which is which. The tester should then try to decide by tasting which is which. The results should be written into a chart.

92 Hygiene and handling food safely

In this section of the book you will learn the following things:

■ how to handle food to prevent cross-contamination;
■ the main causes of food poisoning;
■ storing food carefully to prevent problems.

Bacterial contamination

Some **bacteria** can cause food poisoning. They breed at temperatures between 5°C and 63°C and can multiply very quickly.

To reduce the chances of this happening you must:

■ Always wash your hands really well before and after handling food (Fig 1).

> **Q1** Why is it important to wash your hands well before preparing food?

▲ **Fig 1** Washing your hands.

■ Make sure that the utensils you use, like chopping boards and surfaces, are always clean and disinfected. It is good to keep separate chopping boards for uncooked meats.
■ Never allow raw meat products to come into contact with cooked foods. Do not let uncooked food touch or drip onto other foods in the fridge (Fig 2). Cover foods so that **contamination** by **airborne** bacteria, flies and insects cannot occur.
■ Never let foods stay in warm areas for any length of time because the bacteria will multiply. If food is cooked, it needs to be cooled down quickly to keep bacteria growth to the minimum.

▲ **Fig 2** Incorrect storage in a fridge.

Defrosting

When cooking foods, make sure that they are cooked all the way through. You can use a thermometer to check the temperatures (Fig 3). It is also especially important to thoroughly **defrost** food before cooking. If parts of the meat or poultry are not fully defrosted, then they will never get to a high enough temperature during cooking to kill the bacteria. Cooking will only warm up these areas and let the bacteria multiply to dangerous levels. Food poisoning can kill people – the ill, the elderly and young children are especially at risk.

Make sure that the foods you use are as fresh as possible and have been stored correctly. You may buy a frozen chicken at a supermarket, but its temperature during the journey home may rise before you put it into the **freezer** at home. You must never refreeze meat or **poultry**. Always follow the instructions on the label carefully and never ignore the use by or sell by dates, especially for meat and poultry.

Always wash fruit and vegetables well before use, as many will not be cooked when we eat them, e.g. in salads (Fig 4).

▲ **Fig 3** *Using a thermometer to check the temperature of meat.*

▲ **Fig 4** *Washing fruit and vegetables.*

Q2 Why is important to thaw frozen meat really well?

Q3 What two things are needed for bacteria to multiply quickly?

Key words

airborne – floating around in the air

bacteria – micro-organisms; some can cause food poisoning

contamination – bacteria from other sources getting onto food

defrost – to thaw out, to unfreeze

freezer – a food storage container at -18 °C

poultry – chicken, duck, turkey

SUMMARY

- Hygiene means washing your hands well before handling food.
- Always make sure that your utensils and preparation surfaces are clean.
- Bacteria thrive in warm, damp areas.
- Thaw frozen foods thoroughly.
- Cook foods right through and always follow instructions on the labels.

SUMMARY activity

Collect the labels from two types of frozen meats, and two from frozen vegetables. Are there any differences between the instructions for each type? Write down your answers.

93 Keeping foods for a long time

In this section of the book you will learn the following things:

- what preserving means;
- the methods used for preserving food;
- how the preserving methods work.

There are many ways to keep or preserve food. Some have been used for thousands of years and some are new.

Q1 Why do we need to preserve foods?

There are many reasons for preserving food. For example, when astronauts go on a long journey, the food they will eat must be lightweight,

nourishing and really pleasant to eat. It also has to be easily prepared. Other groups such as soldiers, mountaineers and explorers also need special foods. Foods were originally preserved to provide a supply of things in winter that were only available in summer, or to store excess supplies.

Some processes have been used for many years and are still used today. **Pickling** means mixing with vinegar.

▲ *Fig 1* Some smoked foods.

Salting involves packing meat and fish in layers of salt.
Smoking uses burning wood chips, usually oak, to preserve meat and fish (Fig 1).
Boiling fruit with sugar is another method and is called jamming.

Drying removes the moisture from the produce. Many foodstuffs are dried, e.g. pasta, grains, nuts and rice (Fig 2).

All of these methods affect the micro-organisms' growth in some way, either by reducing moisture or by providing an environment in which they cannot grow.

◀ *Fig 2* Some dried foods.

Years ago, cold streams or ice houses were used to chill food until it was needed. We now have methods to **freeze dry**, **freeze** or **chill** foods the whole year round (Fig 3). Some prepackaged foods, have gases other than air surrounding the food in order to reduce the contamination of the contents.

▲ **Fig 3** *Some frozen and chilled foods.*

Heat is used to kill bacteria in the **bottling** and **canning** processes (Fig 4). Provided the cans are not damaged and bottles stay sealed, the contents will keep for years. Radioactivity can be used to make food products **sterile**. **Irradiated** foods such as tomatoes have been available for some time. These will last without rotting, but people have not been keen to eat food prepared using this method.

◀ **Fig 4** *Some tinned foods.*

Q2 What do preserving methods do to the food?

Q3 What is the most common way we preserve foods in our homes today?

Key words

bottling – sealing food into bottles or jars

canning – sealing food in cans and heating to kill micro-organisms

chill – to cool to below 8°C

freeze – to cool to below −18°C

freeze dry – to remove moisture by freezing

irradiate – use nuclear radiation to sterilise

pickling – preserving with vinegar

salting – packing in layers of salt

smoking – using wood smoke to preserve meat and fish

sterile – with no micro-organisms present

SUMMARY

- Food can be preserved by a variety of methods.
- Some methods have been in use for thousands of years.
- New methods include freeze drying and irradiation.
- Most methods reduce or stop the development of micro-organisms.

SUMMARY *activity*

Prepare a pot noodle as instructed on the label. Taste the food. Make a chart to record your observations. How do the various ingredients compare with the fresh food?

94 Tools for textiles work

In this section of the book you will learn the following things:
- why sewing machines are used;
- the types of textile equipment found in school;
- the equipment that is used for textile work.

Using sewing machines

Although stitching can be done very well by hand, using a **sewing machine** makes the process quicker, gives more strength to the join and can be more accurate. Even simple sewing machines will now do a range of different stitches.

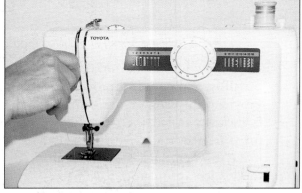

▲ *Fig 1* Threading up a sewing machine.

Q1 Why is using a sewing machine better than hand stitching?

Electronic sewing machines can do a wide range of stitching and some can be connected to a computer. All of them will need setting up according to the thickness and type of fabric on which they are being used (Fig 1). They make the stitch by looping a thread through the material with the needle and joining this thread with another underneath the material. This second thread is held in a **bobbin**, which has to be rewound occasionally (Fig 2). The sewing machine is a precision instrument and therefore needs to be set up to sew correctly. At first, you will need someone to show you how to thread it up. The handbook for the machine will also show you this, and how to adjust it for the correct stitching. You must practise **threading up** and using it on some **samples** of different fabrics to gain experience. The speed of sewing is controlled by a foot control. Care must be taken not to go too fast as this can break the needle, especially if the fabric is thick or heavy.

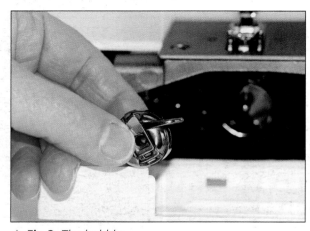

▲ *Fig 2* The bobbin.

▲ *Fig 3* Rewinding the bobbin.

Other large pieces of equipment are knitting machines, overlockers and looms. These are very specialised machines and can often be used with a computer and **CAM** programs.

Small hand tools

You will also need small hand tools such as scissors, pins, needles, tape measures, embroidery frames, hand lens, irons and ironing board (Fig 4).

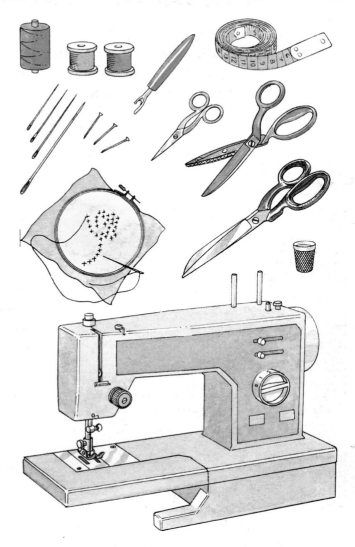

Q2 Where can you find information about using your sewing machine correctly?

Q3 Why must you thread up a sewing machine properly?

▲ **Fig 4** Sewing equipment.

Key words

bobbin – a small spool to hold thread
CAM – computer-aided manufacture
sample – small pieces of fabric
sewing machine – used for joining fabrics using thread
threading up – fitting the thread onto a sewing machine

SUMMARY

■ You may use a range of machines in textiles work.
■ The most common is the sewing machine. It must be carefully threaded and set up before use. You should get someone to show you the first time you use it. If in doubt look at the instruction booklet.
■ There are many small hand tools to cut, join and work textiles. Hand lenses may be useful for examining fabrics.

SUMMARY
activity

Thread up your sewing machine and make a small sample of its range of stitches. Using two samples of fabric, stitch one pair together using the machine and the other pair by hand. Compare them to see which is strongest.

95 Investigating textiles

In this section of the book you will learn the following things:
- how to investigate textiles;
- what you can find out about an artefact;
- how to use the information for your design decisions.

Taking things apart

You can find out lots of information by taking a textile article, such as a shirt, completely to pieces (Fig 1). The main things you can find out about are its **function**, design and **construction** (how it is put together), its structure (the shapes of the individual parts) and, finally, about the materials from which it is made. Take a close look at the fabric with a hand lens to see how it is constructed (Fig 2).

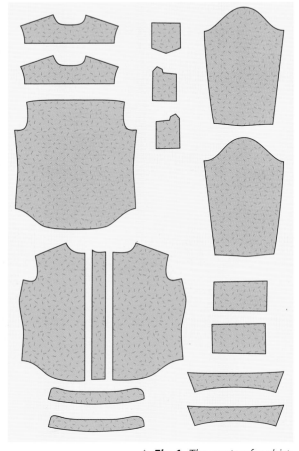

▲ **Fig 1** *The parts of a shirt.*

▲ **Fig 2** *Looking at the weave.*

Q1 Give two reasons for taking a textile to pieces.

When you are starting to look at an **artefact**, you might need to ask the following questions to try to find out about its design, construction, structure, **colour** and materials:

- What is the article designed to do?
- Does it have to do one job or several?
- How well does it do what it is intended to do?
- How does it do it?
- What people would use it?
- How do you decide if it is a successful design?
- What is special about the fabric and why has the designer selected it?

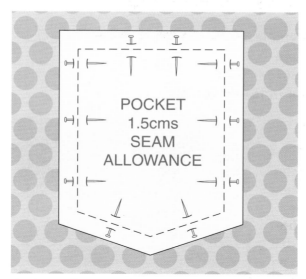

▲ *Fig 3* Allowances for seams.

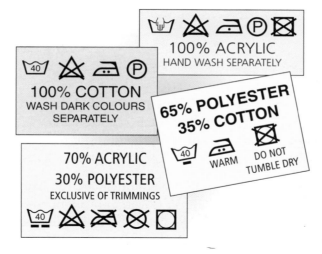

▲ *Fig 4* Labels give you information.

It is important to know how a product is constructed. This can be done by carefully unpicking the stitches. How much extra material is allowed to make up for joins? (Fig 3) How many separate parts is it made from and how are they joined? Is the fabric printed or dyed and **finished**? What are the **fastenings** and decorations? If you are looking at an item of clothing what does the label tell you? (Fig 4) When you are exploring all of these questions, you should draw or take notes about your findings. When you get to the textile itself, this can be **teased apart** so that you can find out how it is constructed. Use a hand lens if necessary.

Q2 Why is it important to know how a garment is put together?

Q3 Why should you try to find out which type of fabric has been used for a particular article?

Key words

artefact – a made article

colour – can be added by dyeing or weaving, for example

construction – how something is made

fastening – buttons, zips, ties, etc

finish – surface treatment of fabric to improve some quality

function – what something is designed to do

tease apart – to gently pull apart

SUMMARY

■ A useful way of finding out about textiles is to take some article completely apart.

■ Try to write down or draw all the things you find out.

■ Often clothes have multiple functions, e.g. they are warm, windproof and rainproof.

■ Look to see how joins are made.

SUMMARY *activity*

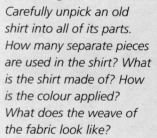

Carefully unpick an old shirt into all of its parts. How many separate pieces are used in the shirt? What is the shirt made of? How is the colour applied? What does the weave of the fabric look like?

96 The fibres used to make textiles

In this section of the book you will learn the following things:
- where natural fibres come from;
- how manufactured fibres are made;
- how materials can be recycled to make fabrics.

Fibres

The **fibres** used in textiles come from two sources: **natural** ones from plants and animals and **manufactured** ones, mainly from oil. The fibres are hair-like and can be very short, called short staple, and need to be twisted together to make longer lengths or they can be in long continuous filaments.

> **Q1** What are the two main sources of fibres?

▲ *Fig 1* *Plant fibres.*

Natural fibres

Those fibres which come from plants are made from different parts of plants. They can be from seed pods which are full of fluffy fibres such as cotton and kapok. They can be from the leaves of a plant (sisal) or from the fibres of the crushed stems, such as linen, jute and hemp (Fig 1).

Those which come from animals are the hair or fur, which is either cut off (sheared) or combed out. Goats, camels, sheep, alpaca and llama are all used, sometimes from special breeds with really long coats. This is usually called wool (Fig 2).

Another source is silk which is a continuous secretion from silk worms which they spin to make their cocoons. The cocoons are soaked in water and unwound (Fig 3). This filament makes a very fine, delicate fabric.

▲ *Fig 2* *Animal wool.*

▲ *Fig 3* *A cocoon and a silkworm.*

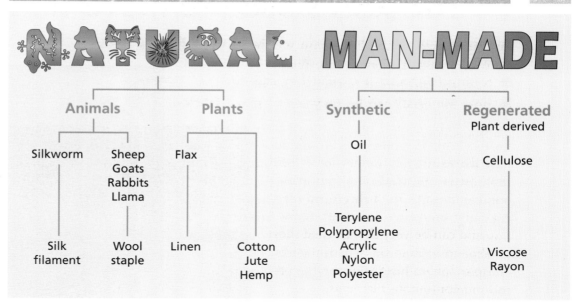

▲ **Fig 4** Sources of fibres.

Manufactured fibres

Manufactured or **synthetic** fibres are forms of plastics made from oil. Various processes are used to make a plastic which can be squeezed through small holes in a **die** to produce a continuous thread.

Cellulose is the building material of all trees and plants. Trees are crushed and the pulp put through chemical processes so just the cellulose remains. This is very much like a plastic. It can be formed into very long filaments.

To make useful fibres which can be knitted or **woven** into fabrics, nearly all are twisted together to make continuous filaments.

Some fibres are recycled by chopping up old clothes and spinning them back into new thread. Plastic soft drink bottles can be recycled into a fluffy material commonly used to make fleeces (Fig 4).

Q2 Why do short staple fibres have to be twisted together?

Q3 Where does cellulose come from?

Key words

die – a metal plate with very small holes through which plastics are squeezed
fibres – hair-like threads
manufactured – made from chemicals and materials such as oil
natural – from sources in nature, plants and animals
synthetic – not occurring naturally
woven – threads joined together to make fabrics

SUMMARY

- Fibres can be short staple or long continuous ones.
- They can come from plants and animals or be man-made.
- Natural fibres come from the seed pods, stems and leaves of plants and from the wool of animals.
- Old clothes or plastics can be recycled into new fibres.

SUMMARY activity

Cut out 50 mm squares of eight different fabrics and staple them to an A4 card. Write down the name of the fabric and whether it is natural or man-made.

97 The properties of fabrics

In this section of the book you will learn the following things:
- why we need fabrics with different properties;
- testing fabrics to see what they can do;
- the various uses of fabrics.

Fibres can be natural, man-made or reconstituted, i.e. recycled. The fibres used to produce fabrics can have many different properties They can be used on their own, such as wool or cotton, or they can be combined to get the best **characteristics** of each, e.g. polyester, cotton or wool, cotton **mixtures**. Sometimes the mixture can save money because an expensive fibre can be partly replaced by a cheaper one without affecting the properties too much (Fig 1).

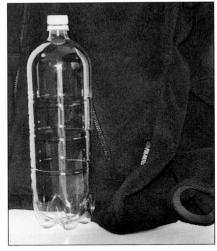

▲ **Fig 1** Fleece made from PET (poly ethylene terepthalate).

Q1 Why do fabrics need different characteristics?

Some of the greatest advances in fabric design have been in the areas of sportswear and outdoor clothing. Some fabrics are weatherproof yet will let perspiration (moisture) disperse through the fabric. Others are very hardwearing yet are very lightweight. Perhaps the most amazing fabrics are those used for astronauts' clothing (Fig 2).

The uppers (tops) of many training shoes are made largely from fabrics. Think about how strong this needs to be – whether dry or wet, cold or hot. It is continually being bent and flexed in all directions (Fig 3).

▲ **Fig 2** Astronaut's clothing.

◀ **Fig 3** Trainers.

The fabric must be carefully chosen so that its characteristics match the needs of the design as closely as possible.

Fabric characteristics

Some fabric characteristics are shown below:

- Strong – does it tear easily?
- **Waterproof** – does it let water through?
- Shrinks – does it get smaller after washing?
- Colourfast – do the colours stay bright after washing?
- Warm – does it help to retain heat?
- Cool – does it keep you cool in the summer?
- Absorbant – does it take up moisture?
- Crease resistant – does it prevent creases forming?
- Stain resistant – does it mark easily?
- **Durable** – does it resist wear? (Fig 4)

Manufacturers will test materials by using machines to pull and stretch a sample thousands of times to see how it will perform when in use.
They may make a machine rub the surface over and over again to see how it will stand up to wear.

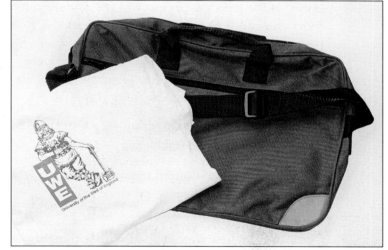

▶ **Fig 4** A sweatshirt and a school bag.

Q2 Which type of clothing needs to be **flameproof**?

Q3 Why does a sweatshirt have to be made from a different material to a school bag?

Key words

characteristics – the properties of a fabric
durable – hard wearing, long lasting
flameproof – resists burning
mixture – using several different types of fibre
waterproof – does not let water through

SUMMARY

- All fibres have their own characteristics.
- They are made into fabrics either of one type or made into mixtures. The mixtures have the advantages of both types of fibre.
- Fabrics can be designed to do a range of tasks. They are chosen because of their characteristics.

SUMMARY activity

Look at some articles made from different fabrics and list three characteristics or properties that each of the fabrics will need to do the job effectively.

98 Putting colour onto fabric

In this section of the book you will learn the following things:
- how fabrics can be coloured;
- the different methods of adding colour;
- the different types of colouring materials,

Dyeing and colouring

Colour can be added to a fabric in lots of different ways. Fibres can be **dyed** before weaving or knitting. They can also be dyed after weaving, or by **painting** or printing onto the fabric's surface. These are the two basic methods: colouring before making up and adding colour after the fabric has been made (Fig 1).

▲ **Fig 1** Colouring before making up and after.

Q1 What are the two ways of adding colour to fabric?

Embroidery uses coloured threads which are sewn through the fabric to produce bright patterns and designs.

Batik uses melted **wax** applied with a **tjanting** to make a pattern on fabric which is then dyed and the wax removed. This can then be repeated – the dye will not soak into the fabric where the wax is (Fig 2). Gutta and Acrobatik are similar processes, but they use products other than wax.

▲ **Fig 2** Batik.

Appliqué builds up designs by attaching coloured fabrics by sewing. Three-dimensional effects can be made by adding thick or textured fabrics.

Fabric crayons, pens or paint let you draw your designs directly onto the fabric. They are usually **fixed** by ironing on the back of the fabric.

Fabric dyes are hot or cold water dyes which can be used on most materials. The fabric is soaked in the dye and then washed. Sometimes the fabric is folded, knotted or tied and then dyed. The dye cannot soak through the tightly knotted parts and this gives the pattern (Fig 3).

Silk paints are used on silk to produce delicate colours. These are often used with quilting to give three-dimensional effects.

Iron-on transfers are designs printed onto paper which can be ironed onto fabrics. If you draw a design using a computer, it can be printed onto **transfer paper**. You must remember to reverse the transfer so when you iron it onto the fabric, it will come out the correct way round (Fig 4).

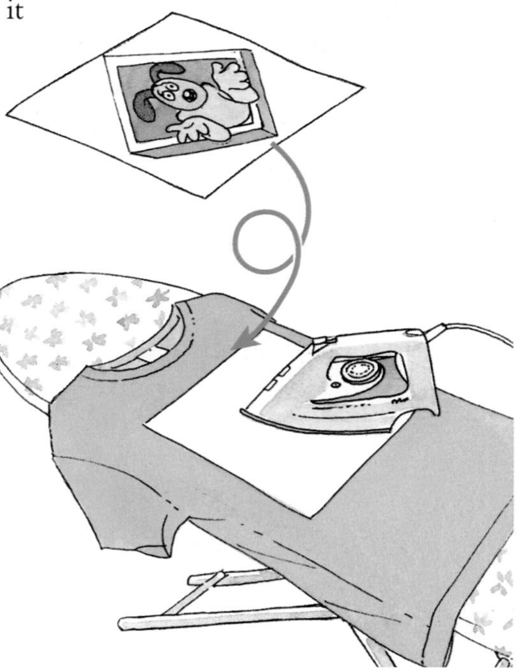

▲ **Fig 3** Tie and dye.

▶ **Fig 4** Ironing-on a transfer.

Puff paints are painted on and then heated using a hairdryer – they swell up into a textured effect.

Stencilling and screen printing use stencils or screens to apply paints only to certain areas of the fabric.

Q2 Why do you need to fix colours?

Q3 Why do you need to reverse the design if you are using transfer paper?

Key words

batik – using wax as a resist before dyeing
dye – colour which soaks through the material
fixing – helps to prevent dyes washing out of fabrics
paint – colour which is applied to the surface of materials
tjanting – the tool for applying wax in batik
transfer paper – colour designs can be transferred onto fabric by ironing
wax – melted onto fabric to stop dyes from soaking in

SUMMARY

- Colours can be added to fabrics before weaving or knitting.
- There are many different ways of adding colour.
- Dyes soak into materials, whilst paints are applied to the surface.

SUMMARY activity

Use fabric crayons to design a small coloured picture for ironing onto a T-shirt.

99 Labelling

In this section of the book you will learn the following things:
- why fabrics are labelled;
- what information labels on fabrics tell you;
- what the symbols on labels tell you.

Symbols and pictograms

Labels are attached to all textiles to tell you what they are made from and how to treat them. Some labels also tell you that the fabrics have special qualities such as fire or **stain resistance**. Labels often have **symbols** or **pictograms** on them so that they can be easily understood by anyone, even in another country (Fig 1).

Q1 What two things about fabrics do labels tell you?

Washing fabrics

There are many different fabrics available. Some are man-made, some are natural and it is sometimes not easy to tell one from another. So, when they get dirty and need to be cleaned, it is also difficult to know how to do it. There are many washing powders and detergents available and choosing the correct ones can be a problem (Fig 2). Fabrics can be damaged by using the wrong washing or ironing temperatures. Some fabrics need to be dry cleaned, i.e. using chemical solvents instead of water. This cannot be done in the home, but must be done by professional cleaners.

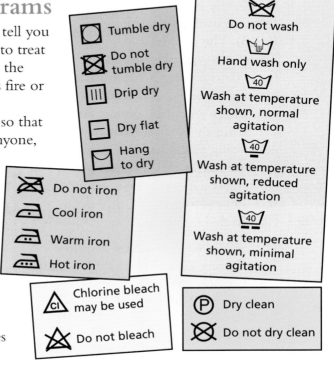

▲ **Fig 1** The symbols on care labels.

▲ **Fig 2** Some of the many cleaning agents available.

Some fabrics have special **finishes** applied, which would be removed by washing at too high a temperature. Children's nightdresses and pyjamas often have **flame retardent** finishes which may be removed by frequent washing (Fig 3). The dyes in some fabrics can run and can colour other fabrics in the same wash – labels often tell you to wash these fabrics on their own. Labels are also very important advertising tools, sometimes they are fixed to the outside of clothing to let everyone know that you are wearing clothes by famous designers.

Safety

There are labels on furniture to say that the foam and fabrics used have passed Fire and Safety regulations. This is important as many materials used today are types of plastic and when they burn, they can give off lethal fumes. They are treated with chemicals to reduce this happening.

▲ **Fig 3** Flame retardant children's clothing.

Q2 What could happen to a fabric if it was washed or ironed at too high a temperature?

Q3 Why do you have to wash some fabrics separately?

Key words

finish – coating put onto fabrics to improve their characteristics

flame retardant – fabric is chemically protected against the risk of fire

pictograms – drawings of certain actions like ironing, washing, etc

stain resistant – fabric that is chemically protected against stains affecting the fibres

symbols – drawings which represent things

SUMMARY

- There are many different types of fabrics and finishes used in clothes and furniture.
- Labels tell you how to handle these fabrics and how to wash, iron, clean and treat them.
- They tell you the materials from which the fabric is made and indicate any special finishes such as fire resistance.

SUMMARY activity

Make a chart of the information found on labels in six pieces of your clothing. Include references to temperature, ways of washing, fibre content and any special finishes.

100 How artefacts are made

In this section of the book you will learn the following things:

- how fabrics are joined together;
- how shapes are made;
- temporary and permanent joining.

Shapes are made by cutting out a paper **pattern** and pinning the parts together to test if the resulting shape is suitable for the design or fit required. When this is satisfactory, the pattern can be transferred onto fabric, cut out and the edges joined together by stitching (Fig 1).

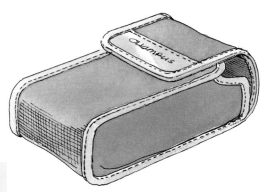

▲ *Fig 1* A textile camera case.

> **Q1** Why is it a good idea to make a paper pattern before cutting the fabric?

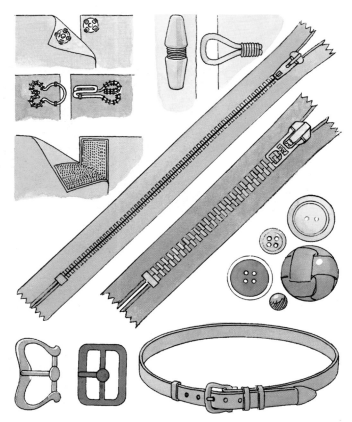

▲ *Fig 2* Different fasteners.

Fabrics are joined together in lots of different ways, such as **tacking** and machining, in order to give the shape of the required object. Tacking is using large stitches which are just to hold the material together to check the fit.

These joins are **temporary** to help with the construction and are removed when the article has been **permanently stitched**. There are a variety of ways of closing or fastening fabrics such as buttons, toggles, velcro, hooks and eyes and zips (Fig 2).

> **Q2** Why do we tack things together at first?
>
> **Q3** Why is a 1.5 cm seam allowance important?

When fabrics are joined together, you lose some material making the join, so the pattern needs to be bigger than the finished size. You need to add at least 1.5 cm to all edges. This is called the **seam allowance**.

Cut edges are turned up and **hemmed** to prevent them fraying.

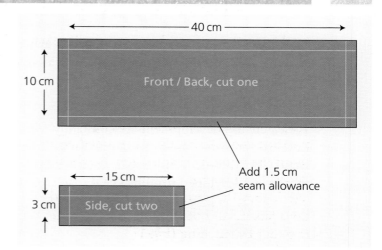

▲ **Fig 3** *Pattern for the camera case.*

Other joining methods

Although sewing is the most common method of joining fabrics, they can be glued together, or bonded together by melting a plastic web (Bondaweb) or powder between the two pieces of fabric using an iron. As a lot of fabrics are made of plastic fibres, they can be welded together by using heat or **ultrasonics**. The sails of sailing dinghies are often joined this way. Wet weather clothes such as cagoules also use the same principle to join the various parts (Fig 4).

▶ **Fig 4** *Wet weather and sailing gear.*

Key words

allowance – extra fabric to allow for seams
hem – used to stop fabric fraying on cut edges
pattern – a paper shape to test designs
permanent stitch – the final strong stitching
seam – used to join fabrics together
tack – to join together with a removable stitch
temporary stitch – a stitch that just holds things together and is removed later
ultrasonics – vibrating things together until they heat up and melt

SUMMARY

- Patterns are used to test designs.
- They are also used to cut out the fabric to the correct size. A seam allowance of 1.5 cm should be added on the pattern to all joins or seams.
- Fabrics can be joined in different ways: sewing, gluing and for some man-made types, welding using heat or ultrasonics.

SUMMARY activity

Make a paper pattern for a small case to hold a camera or a Walkman. It should have a fastening flap. Remember to add 1.5 cm to all edges for seams and hems.

101 New types of textiles

In this section of the book you will learn the following things:

■ what types of new materials are available;
■ what are their characteristics;
■ what they are used for.

Research and development are constantly taking place and new textiles are being developed for new uses. It is important to know and understand where some of these fabrics come from so that we know how to use them. Quite a lot of new fabrics are developed from recycled materials such as plastic bottles (Fig 1).

Wash bottle → Shred or flake it → Melt or dissolve → Spin into fibres → Make into fleece, T-shirts, carpets

▲ **Fig 1** From plastic bottle to fleece.

▲ **Fig 2** The sail is made from shiny transparent fabric.

Nearly all new materials are based on **polymers**, i.e. plastic-based materials.

These new fabrics may have all the characteristics of older fibres such as wool, but also new ones such as breathability, shiny surfaces, very lightweight and smooth finishes (Fig 2).

Many polymers can be made into transparent fibres, so the fabrics produced can be extremely lightweight, shiny and see-through.

Q1 What are most new materials made from?

Kevlar is a lightweight material which is very strong – so strong that it can be used in bullet-proof vests and boat sails.

Lycra (elastine) is a very stretchy material which is used for swimming costumes, and cycle pants. It is a man-made material with the characteristics of rubber.

Polyester fibre and film are used for sails on dinghies and sailboards. Polyester fibre is a plastic woven cloth and when used for sails it is rolled between heated rollers to melt the surface to prevent it being porous. This is called **hot rolling**. Sometimes a similar effect is produced by coating the fabric with a glue-like substance.

Rip-stop nylon is also used for sails, and instead of being stitched, it is often welded together using heat. It is very difficult to tear.

Outdoor clothing for sports and workwear requires the textiles from which they are made to be breathable. Materials such as Goretex and Tactel rely on using these new fabrics in many thin layers, allowing them to be lightweight and comfortable to wear even when exercising or working outdoors in bad weather.

Microfibres are so closely woven that they will not allow water in but allow perspiration to escape In the future, **smart materials** will allow fabrics to change colour using electronics (Fig 4).

Q2 What sorts of characteristics can new materials have?

Q3 What is the main characteristic of outdoor clothing?

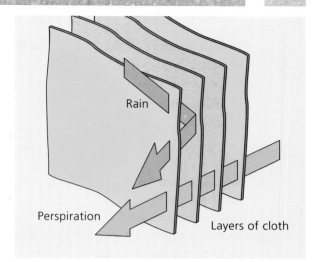

▲ **Fig 3** Fabric requirements for outdoor clothing.

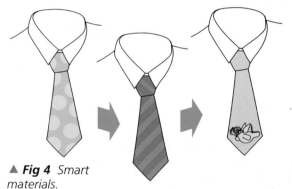

▲ **Fig 4** Smart materials.

Key words

hot rolling – melting the outer surfaces of plastic fabrics

kevlar – a very strong fabric

lycra – a stretchy fabric

microfibres – closely woven materials

polymers – chains of plastic molecules

smart materials – new materials with unusual characteristics

SUMMARY

- New fibres are derived from plastics.
- Most development is done in sports and outdoor clothing or workwear.
- The new fibres are lighter in weight, breathable, shiny and some are transparent.
- Fabrics can be lightweight, so many layers with different characteristics can be put together to make a thin cloth with amazing properties.

▶ **Fig 5** A star profile for a fleece.

SUMMARY *activity*

Use two different items of sports or outdoor clothing and make up star profiles to describe their characteristics as in Fig 5.

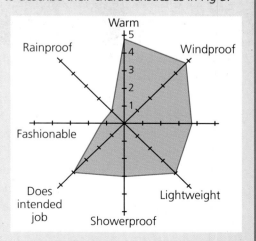

102 Quality

In this section of the book you will learn the following things:
- what quality means;
- how the idea of quality can vary;
- using materials which do not damage the environment.

Satisfying the need

We all use the word quality as if it only had one meaning, i.e. top of the range, most expensive (Fig 1). The real meaning is judging something by how well it does the job that it was designed to do.

▲ **Fig 1** Quality goods?

Q1 What does quality mean?

A quality bicycle used in a large city may be different to one in a Third World country village. The **need** is different. In the first, it may be used only for leisure where spares and repairs are easily available. In the second, it may have to work on dry, dusty roads with little chance of repair or spares if it breaks down. If the bike was the only method of transport for the local doctor or nurse to visit their patients in villages, then a breakdown could be a matter of life or death (Fig 2). The needs of the **users** are totally different, so quality can mean different things to different people. The user's needs for the first may be: to be good looking, have many gears and a cool image. In the second, it may be total reliability, able to work for a long time with little maintenance and able to carry lots of luggage.

▲ **Fig 2** Transport at home and in the Third World.

Environmentally friendly?

How well an item uses **resources** may be another requirement. If a material is in short supply, very expensive or comes from a non-renewable source, are there other materials which can be used? In some Far Eastern countries, cycle frames have been made from bamboo because it is easily available. It is very important to use efficiently materials that can be recycled, that come from renewable resources and that are made using processes which do not harm the world, its animals or people (Fig 3). Your materials should have minimum **environmental impact**.

When making your project, you should try to keep the idea of quality in your mind at all times. Try to make your project as **aesthetically** pleasing as possible to the user. This means that besides doing the job as well as possible it should be pleasing to feel, look at and use. If it is a food project, it should be pleasant both in flavour and texture as well as looking attractive (Fig 4).

◀ *Fig 3* Pollution.

Q2 If you were buying a bike, what points would you look for?

Q3 What are renewable sources?

▶ *Fig 4* Aesthetically pleasing presentation.

Key words

aesthetics – to do with how good something is

environmental impact – how much effect something has on the world

need – a requirement

resources – available materials

user – the person who will use the product or service

SUMMARY

■ Quality means satisfying the needs of the user. This means that ideas of quality can be different.

■ Resources which are non-renewable should not be used.

■ Your projects should be quality projects.

SUMMARY *activity*

Cut out six pictures of different products from magazines. Write down what you think makes them quality products.

103 Health and safety

In this section of the book you will learn the following things:
- the need to find out and assess risks;
- how to reduce the risks to yourself and others;
- using safety equipment and taking precautions.

When making projects or working in workshops, your safety and that of others is very important. This means that not only are you responsible for ensuring that you are safe, but that what you are doing will not cause danger for anyone nearby. Before starting to do something, you should think about the safety requirements needed. Often the things that we do regularly are the ones we do not think carefully enough about. Think carefully about every aspect. Know, remember and follow the rules at all times (Fig 1).

Q1 Why do you need to think about safety?

When beginning any work, you need to think about the **risks** and possible **hazards**:

- Are there any problems with the materials? Are they heavy, slippery, hot, etc?
- Does working with the materials cause dust, **swarf**, fumes or hygiene problems?
- What are the problems using the tools, machinery or utensils?
- What are the hazards in workshops or home economics rooms?
- Could any part of my clothes, hair or jewellery get caught in anything?
- Dust and fumes can cause problems and can be **cumulative**.
- What are you going to do to reduce the risks?

You should **assess** the risks. In the workshop/kitchens there may be hot parts of machinery/cookers, hot liquids and chemicals, obstructions and hard surfaces. If you run around, you may slip and fall (Fig 2).

▲ *Fig 1* Some safety rules.

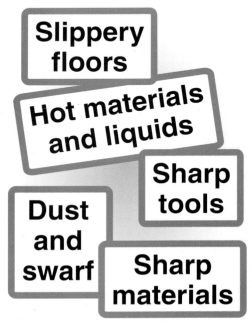

▲ *Fig 2* Spot the safety hazards.

Make sure that any items such as tools, containers, heavy materials or hot liquids are not put near the edges of benches/tables or cookers where they can be easily knocked off.

Tie up your hair. Do not wear clothes with loose sleeves. Take off rings and jewellery.

Wearing and using safety equipment

You should wear the proper safety equipment, e.g. goggles, face masks, aprons or gloves. They will protect you from heat, flying swarf or dust and spills of chemicals. They should be in good condition (Fig 3).

▲ *Fig 3* Safety equipment.

Before using any equipment, make sure that you have been shown how to use it safely.

If you are unsure about any aspect of safety, you should ask your teacher for advice.

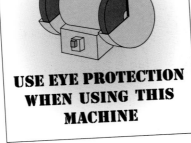

DANGER

USE EYE PROTECTION WHEN USING THIS MACHINE

Often, around your classrooms there will be information posters about safety. Read them carefully and act on them (Fig 4).

REMEMBER HYGIENE

Wash your hands.
Keep your workspace clean.
Prevent cross contamination.
Keep food cool.

Q2 When should you wear safety equipment?

Q3 What can you do if you are unsure about any safety rules?

◄ *Fig 4* Posters about safety.

Key words

assess – to try to work out
cumulative – adds up over time
hazard – a danger
risk – a possible danger
swarf – metal shavings

SUMMARY

- You need to recognise the risks when doing practical work.
- You should take care to protect yourself and others around you.
- You should always wear the proper safety equipment.
- Read any information about safety and act upon it.

SUMMARY activity
Make a safety badge to remind people about being careful in the workshops/kitchens.

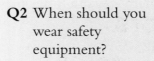

Useful formulae and tables

Electronics

Ohms Law

$E = IR$ sometimes writen as $V = IR$

$$I = \frac{V}{R}$$

$$R = \frac{V}{I}$$

Where E or V = voltage in volts, I = current in amps, R = resistance in ohms.

Power

Watts = $E \times I$ or   Watts = $V \times I$

Watts = $I^2 \times R$

$$\text{Watts} = \frac{V^2}{R}$$

Resistor values

Resistors are measured in ohms and the normal range goes from 1 ohm up to about 4.7 million ohms, i.e. 4.7 megohms, although higher values are sometimes used.

K = kilo = 1000 ohms so 4K7 is 4700 ohms or 4.7 kilohms, 47K is 47000 ohms or 47 kilohms.

M = meg = 1000000 ohms so 1M2 is 1200000 ohms or 1.2 megohms, 12M is 12000000 ohms or 12 megohms.

Resistors in series

$R_{\text{total}} = R_1 + R_2 + R_3 + \ldots$

Resistors in parallel

$$R_{\text{total}} = \frac{1}{R_1} + \frac{1}{R_2} + \frac{1}{R_3} + \ldots$$

Capacitors in series

$$C_{\text{total}} = \frac{1}{C_1} + \frac{1}{C_2} + \frac{1}{C_3} + \ldots$$

The working voltages add up, so two 16 vw (volt working) add up to to 32 vw (volt working), and can have the higher voltage across them. Make sure that the polarity is correct if using an electrolytic or tantalum capacitor.

Capacitors in parallel

$C_{\text{total}} = C_1 + C_2 + C_3 + \ldots$

The maximum working voltage is the lowest of all the capacitors, so if you have three capacitors with 6 volts vw, 9 vw, 12 vw in parallel then the overall working voltage is 6 volts.

Capacitor values

Capacitors are measured in farads named after Faraday. The normal sizes used are much smaller and are measured in microfarads, i.e. a millionth of a farad.

$$1 \text{ microfarad} = 1 \text{ mfd} = \frac{1}{1\,000\,000} \text{ farad}$$

$$1 \text{ nanofarad} = 1 \text{ nfd} = \frac{1}{1\,000\,000\,000} \text{ farad}$$

$$1 \text{ picofarad} = 1 \text{ pfd} = \frac{1}{1\,000\,000\,000\,000} \text{ farad}$$

Mathematical formulae

Area = length $\times$ width

Volume = length $\times$ width $\times$ thickness

Structures

Moment of force = force $\times$ distance

Stress/pressure = force $\times$ area

Mechanical advantage = $\dfrac{\text{load}}{\text{effort}}$ or   MA = $\dfrac{L}{E}$

For levers

Velocity ratio = $\dfrac{\text{distance moved by effort}}{\text{distance moved by load}}$

For gears

Velocity ratio = $\dfrac{\text{number of driven teeth}}{\text{number of driver teeth}}$

For levers

Velocity ratio = $\dfrac{\text{diameter of driven pulley}}{\text{diameter of driver pulley}}$

Ergonome

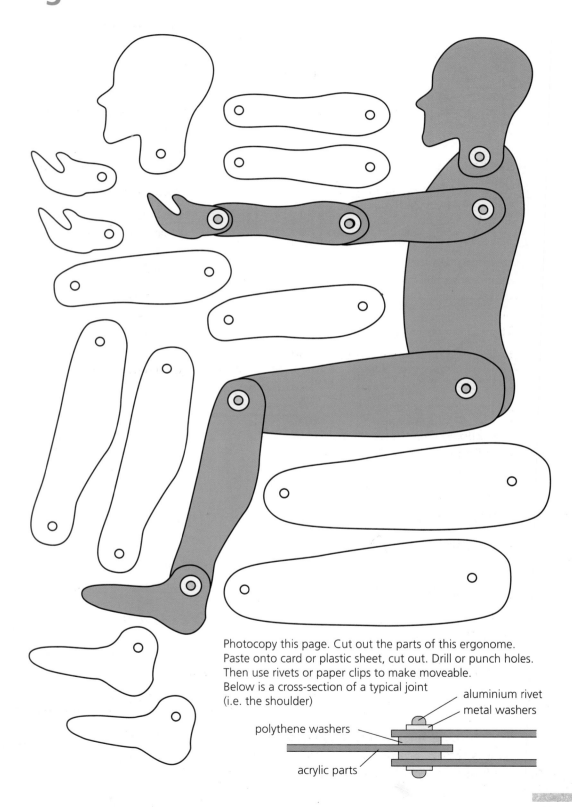

Photocopy this page. Cut out the parts of this ergonome.
Paste onto card or plastic sheet, cut out. Drill or punch holes.
Then use rivets or paper clips to make moveable.
Below is a cross-section of a typical joint
(i.e. the shoulder)

aluminium rivet
metal washers
polythene washers
acrylic parts

Small hand tools

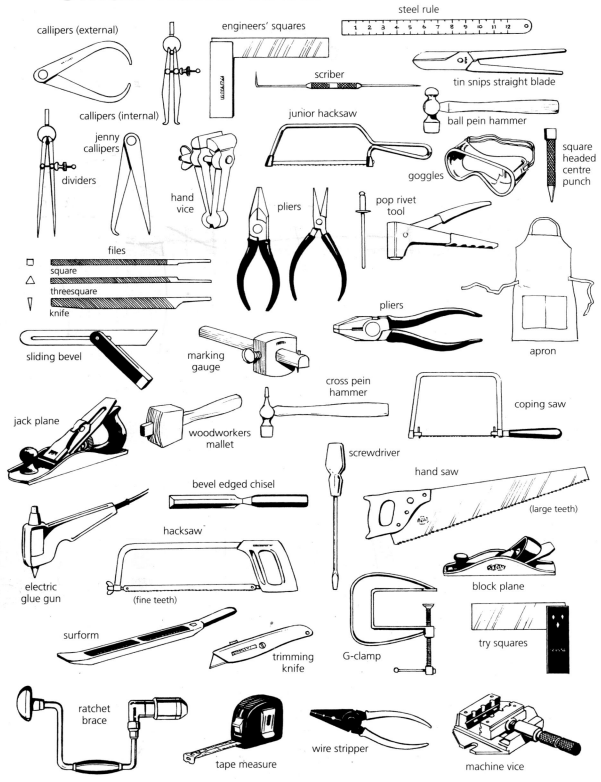

callipers (external)

engineers' squares

steel rule

1 2 3 4 5 6 7 8 9 10 11 12

scriber

tin snips straight blade

callipers (internal)

junior hacksaw

ball pein hammer

jenny callipers

goggles

square headed centre punch

dividers

hand vice

pliers

pop rivet tool

files

square

△ threesquare

∇ knife

pliers

apron

sliding bevel

marking gauge

cross pein hammer

coping saw

jack plane

woodworkers mallet

screwdriver

hand saw

bevel edged chisel

(large teeth)

electric glue gun

hacksaw

(fine teeth)

block plane

surform

trimming knife

G-clamp

try squares

ratchet brace

tape measure

wire stripper

machine vice

Resistor colour code

4 band resistor

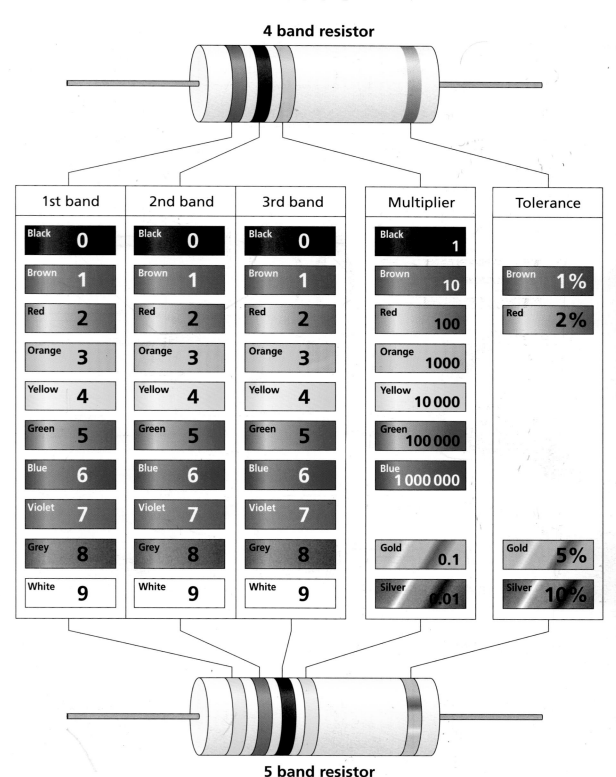

1st band	2nd band	3rd band	Multiplier	Tolerance
Black 0	Black 0	Black 0	Black 1	
Brown 1	Brown 1	Brown 1	Brown 10	Brown 1%
Red 2	Red 2	Red 2	Red 100	Red 2%
Orange 3	Orange 3	Orange 3	Orange 1000	
Yellow 4	Yellow 4	Yellow 4	Yellow 10 000	
Green 5	Green 5	Green 5	Green 100 000	
Blue 6	Blue 6	Blue 6	Blue 1 000 000	
Violet 7	Violet 7	Violet 7		
Grey 8	Grey 8	Grey 8	Gold 0.1	Gold 5%
White 9	White 9	White 9	Silver 0.01	Silver 10%

5 band resistor

Symbols for pneumatic devices

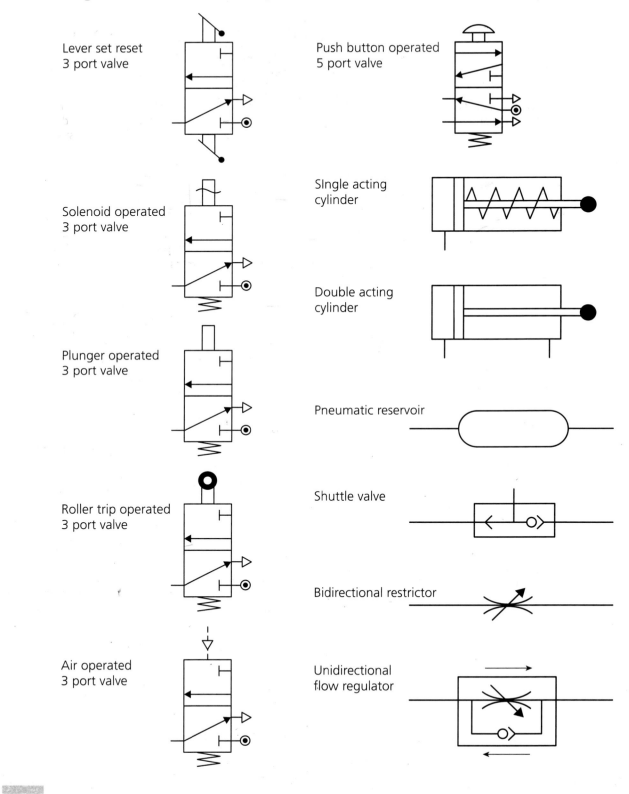

Lever set reset
3 port valve

Solenoid operated
3 port valve

Plunger operated
3 port valve

Roller trip operated
3 port valve

Air operated
3 port valve

Push button operated
5 port valve

Single acting
cylinder

Double acting
cylinder

Pneumatic reservoir

Shuttle valve

Bidirectional restrictor

Unidirectional
flow regulator

Electronic component symbols

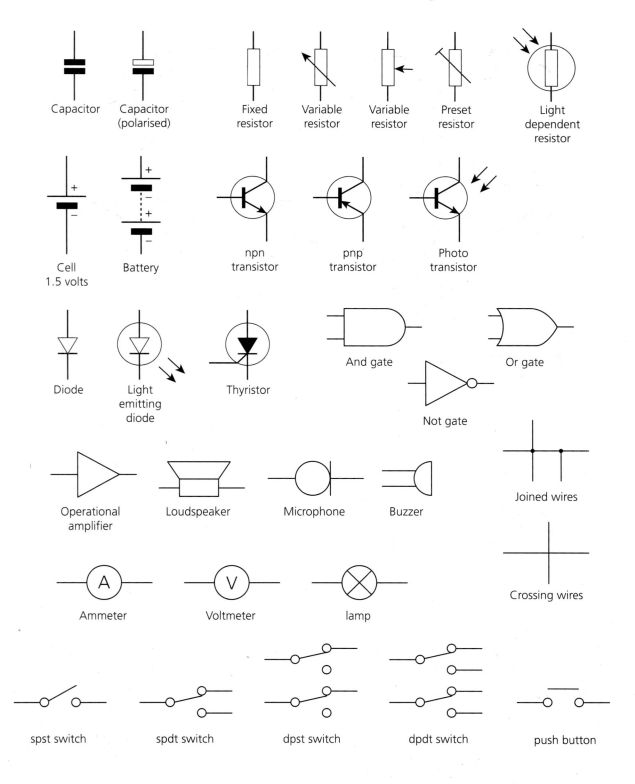

Capacitor

Capacitor (polarised)

Fixed resistor

Variable resistor

Variable resistor

Preset resistor

Light dependent resistor

Cell 1.5 volts

Battery

npn transistor

pnp transistor

Photo transistor

Diode

Light emitting diode

Thyristor

And gate

Or gate

Not gate

Operational amplifier

Loudspeaker

Microphone

Buzzer

Joined wires

Crossing wires

Ammeter

Voltmeter

lamp

spst switch

spdt switch

dpst switch

dpdt switch

push button

Name

Isometric grid

Name

Web links

Use these sites for help with planning and researching projects or for background reading and general interest.

Design and Technology: General

http://www.dtonline.org

http://www.technologyindex.com

http://www.technology.org.uk

http://www.berkley7.freeserve.co.uk

http://www.howstuffworks.com

http://www.kented.org.uk/ngfl/websites/tech.html

http://www.telegraph.co.uk/etc/iefedwebdt.html

Mechanisms

http://www.cabaret.co.uk

http://www.flying-pig.co.uk

http://www.smithautomata.co.uk

http://www.sagecraft.com/puppetry

http://www.ntrsa.nl/~mgoris/mechtoys

Electronics

http://www.new-wave-concepts.com

http://www.doctronics.co.uk

http://www.us-espanorama.net/index.htmil

Plastics

http://www.geplastics.com/resins/education/cartoon.html

Making PCBs

http://www.niche.co.uk

Alternative Technology

 http://www.cat.org.uk

Food

http://www.milk.co.uk

http://www.nutrition.org.uk

http://www.birdseye.com/nutrition.html

http://www.foodandhealth.com/foodlinks.html

http://www.safeway.co.uk/about/food

Textiles

http://www.hiraeth.com/ytg/proj_index.htm

http://www.hiraeth.com/ytg/links.htm

http://www.kidsdomain.com/craft

http://www.quilting.about.com/hobbies/quilting

Museums

http://www.designmuseum.org

http://www.24hourmuseum.org

http://www.museumfortextiles.on.ca

Note
Although these sites have been chosen for their integrity and educational value, Letts Educational is not responsible for their content or that of any linked site.

Glossary

A

abrasive – a material which can wear others away

actuator – a device which operates something

aesthetics – the artistic, tastefulness and beauty of the product

airborne – floating around in the air

allowance – extra fabric to allow for seams

alloys – a mixture of two or more metals

amplifier – a circuit which makes small signals larger

amplitude – height of a signal

analogue signal – a signal which is changing in amplitude

analysis – finding out

annealing – making metal softer and easier to work

anthropometric data – data about the sizes and measurement of people, what they can reach, and hold, etc

artefact – a manufactured object

automata – model figures which move when handles are turned

axis – the centre of rotation

B

bacteria – micro-organisms; some can cause food poisoning

balanced diet – a diet giving all or most of the nutrients needed

batch production – making a small number of a product

batik – using wax as a resist

bellcrank – a lever with an angle at the fulcrum

bibliography – a list of sources of information

bond – joining together using glue

brainstorming – a technique for writing down linked ideas quickly

brazing – a high temperature join using spelter

breadboard – a board for building circuits on

brief – a short statement about what you intend to do

browser – a program which allows you to access the internet

bubble diagram – a diagram of your ideas

buffer box – helps you connect inputs and outputs to a computer easily

bulking – providing mass or volume

C

CAD – computer-aided design

CAM – computer-aided manufacture

cam – a shaped disc or eccentric wheel

cantilever – a beam supported only at one end

capacitor – a device which stores charge

carbohydrates – sugars and starches

carbon fibre – a resin with carbon threads in it

carbon steel – steel with carbon added which can be tempered

CAT – computer-aided testing

CD-ROM – Compact Disk Read Only Memory

characteristics – the qualities of a material or ingredient

chill – to cool to below 8°C

circuit symbol – the drawing which represents the component in a circuit diagram

clamping – forcing two materials together using a G-clamp or vice

Clipart – graphics from CD-ROMs and the Internet which can be added to your work

closed loop – a system with feedback

CMOS – complementary metal oxide semiconductor

compliant materials– textiles, paper

components – parts of a project

composite – a mixture of two or more materials

concept map – a map of understanding and learning

coniferous – tree which has cones; usually an evergreen

context – where the design need occurs

control language – special commands to help you give instructions for control

conversion – cutting timber into useful sizes

corrugation – putting a series of folds into paper or card

crating – using lightly drawn boxes for guidance

criteria – requirements which must be met

cross-section – the cut face showing when you cut through something

curing – heating a resin to set it

D

data – any information which is in a spreadsheet or database

database – a program which links together information which can then be searched

deciduous – tree which loses its leaves in winter; broad leafed

design brief – a short statement about what is needed, who it is for, and any constraints

design processes – stages in putting your thoughts into a structure

designer – the person who devises what the product will be like

designing – thinking of and developing ideas

digital camera – a camera which takes pictures which are stored in digital form

digital signal – a signal which has two states: on or off

dimension – to add measurements to drawings

diode – a device which passes current in one direction

disassembly – taking things to pieces

DMA – design and make assignment

DMT – design and make task

double-acting – air pressure pushes piston out and in

download – to send information to your computer from the Internet or cameras, etc

DPDT – double pole double throw

DPST – double pole single throw

draft angle – an angle which helps the pattern to release from the vacuum form

drive belts – soft rubber or plastic materials used with pulleys

dye – a chemical colour

dynamic – a changing load

E

eccentric cam – a circular cam with offset axis

effort – the force put into a system

elastic limit – when materials are stretched, they return to their original length, unless they have been stretched beyond the elastic limit

elevation – a view

environmental impact – how much effect something has on the world

ergonome – a scale model of the human body with flexible joints

ergonomic data – data about how people relate to the things they use

evaluate – to compare with the specification

exploded diagrams – showing how all the parts fit together

F

fabrication – making up something from materials

fat – found in meat, milk, cheese and butter

feedback – taking some of the output back to the input

fibre – contained in food from plants

fibres – threads from which fabrics are made

fixed scale – where things are made to certain scales, such as model trains

fixing – helps to prevent dyes washing out of fabrics

flame retardant – fabric is chemically protected against the risk of fire

flavour – the taste of a product

flow diagrams – shows the organisation of projects

flux – a paste which stops oxygen from affecting metals when heated

focused – task which has a clearly defined result

follower – a slider which rubs on the outside edge of a cam

formative evaluation – an on-going evaluation

former – a pattern around which materials can be shaped

found materials – those which we normally throw away (scrap)

framed structure – a framework of parts

freehand – drawing without using rules or straight edges

freeze dry – to remove moisture by freezing

friction – occurs when two surfaces rub against each other

fulcrum – a pivot point

G

garnish – to decorate food using colours, textures, etc

gate – a device which switches depending upon its inputs

gear ratio – a comparison of the number of teeth on the output and input gears

glaze – a coating of egg, sugar solution or stock to provide a shine on food

green timber – newly felled timber containing a lot of moisture

GRP – glass reinforced plastics sometimes called glass fibre

H

hardwood – wood from a tree that loses its leaves in winter

hazard – a danger

heat bending – using heat to bend thermoplastics

heatsink – a metal plate used to remove heat from semiconductors

hem – used to stop fabric fraying on cut edges

high tensile steel – a very strong type of steel

high – a 1 logic state, voltage present

hydraulics – using compressed fluid, usually a special oil, to move things

I

idler gear – a small gear fitted in between two gears so that they turn in the same direction

implication – what is going to happen as a result of a decision taken

ingredients – the individual parts of a recipe or food

inputs – sensors, i.e. switches which produce an electrical output

integrated circuits – small electronic circuits, ICs

interference – noise which stops information getting through

irradiate – use nuclear radiation to sterilise

irreversible – once something has been done, it cannot be changed

isometric grid – grid with vertical lines and at 30° to horizontal

iterative process – process of constant assessment and improvement

J

jig – a device to hold odd shaped work

K

kilohm – one thousand ohms

knot – a round dark part of timber, where a branch starts in the tree

L

lag – the time it takes a system to respond to change

laminating – gluing together thin strips of material to make a thicker one

LDR – light-dependent resistor

LED – light-emitting diode

lever – a rod pivoted along its length

linear – a straight line

load – the forces acting on a structure

Log – logarithmic resistance track

logic – representing signals at 0 or 1 states

low – a 0 logic state, no voltage present

M

machine – a device which does work using moving and fixed components

mass production – making very large quantities of products

mass structure – a structure which resists forces with its own weight

MDF – medium density fibreboard

mechanical advantage – how much the effort is amplified

mechanisms – a system of gears, cams, pulleys working together

megohm – one million ohms

mesh – to link or fit together

microcontroller – a small programmable computer on a single chip

microfibres – closely woven materials

milling machine – a machine which can cut and shape metals, or thick plastics

minerals – found in vegetables and fruit, keeps you healthy

mock up – a model

modelling – making small scale replicas or using a computer program to test ideas

monomers – the smallest part of a plastic material

mould – molten metal is poured into this to make a shape

multimedia – sound, pictures, text, video in digital form

N

N type – negative type semiconductor

natural – from sources in nature, plants and animals

NTC – negative temperature coefficient

nutrient – ingredients which are beneficial to life

O

on/off switch – switch with only two states called on or off, sometimes shown as 1 or 0

open loop – a system without feedback

open task – task which can have varied or unknown end results

operator – the method in which the valve is operated, e.g. push button, lever, etc

orthographic drawing – a style of drawing with measurements and construction details

outcome – the result of a design activity

outputs – devices which light up, sound or move when a voltage is applied

oxidising – oxides forming when a metal is heated

P

P type – positive type semiconductor

packaging – the containers in which products are sold

PCB – a printed circuit board

permanent stitch – the final strong stitching

perspective – giving the impression of depth

photosynthesis – the process in plants of making glucose by using energy from the sun

PIC – peripheral interface controller, the microcontroller

pickling – preserving with vinegar

pictograms – drawings of certain actions like ironing, washing, etc

pictorial drawing – a realistic, rendered drawing of the project

piezoelectric – a material which can change shape when a voltage is applied, and vice versa

pilot hole – a small hole used to stop materials splitting when using nails or screws

pinion – a smaller gear

pivot point – a point of rotation

planishing – hammering the surface of sheet metal

plastic memory – when reheated thermoplastics try to return to their previous shape

pneumatics – using compressed air to move things

polymer – a molecule formed when monomers are joined together

polystyrene foam – a thermoplastic material used for modelling

port – where air enters and leaves a pneumatic component

potentiometer – a variable resistor

precious metals – rare metals such as gold, silver and platinum

presentation drawings – coloured drawings which show the product as if in 3D

preserve – to keep fruit or vegetables from spoiling

preset resistor – a screwdriver operated variable resistor

primary research – research which you collect

prioritise – the order in which things need to be done

product – the finished article

programmable – a chip that can be loaded with a program and run

programmer – a device which programs computer chips

properties – the characteristics of a material or ingredient

proposals – the things you intend to do

protein – body building material

prototype – a model to test an idea before production

PTC – positive temperature coefficient

pulley – a wheel with a groove in its rim for a belt to run in

pulse width – the time a digital signal is on or off

pulses – a general word for beans, peas and lentils

PVA – poly vinyl acetate

Q

quality assurance – making sure products are up to standard

questionnaire – a list of questions with spaces for written answers

R

reconciliation – deciding to do things in a way that may not be your first choice

recycling – reusing waste or unwanted materials

regulator – controls the maximum pressure to part of a system

relay – a solenoid operated switch

research – finding out information

resistant materials – wood, metal and plastics

rub-down transfers – prepared, etch-resistant, component pads which can be rubbed on to the clean copper surface of a PCB

S

salting – packing in layers of salt

scale – the size of the model compared to the real thing

seam – used to join fabrics together

seasoning – reducing the moisture content of timber

secondary research – research collected and published by others

semiconductor – a silicon-based material or electronic component

sensors – devices that can sense temperature, heat, light and moisture

shear – a force which acts across a material

shell structure – a structure made of sheet materials

simulate – use the computer to try out something before actually making it

single-acting – in a pneumatic circuit air pressure pushes piston out, a spring returns it

sketching – drawing freehand

SMA – Shape Metal Alloy

Smart or buffer box – a box connected to a computer, which enables you to plug in inputs and output devices easily

smart materials – new materials with unusual characteristics.

snail cam – a snail-shaped cam

soft jaws – soft plastic jaws to fit in a vice to prevent marking the surfaces being held

softwood – wood from a tree which keeps its leaves in winter

solvents – chemical which dissolves others

sources – where you find information

SPDT – single pole double throw

specification – what the product has to do and look like, a list of design requirements

spreadsheet program – a computer program such as *Excel* which stores data and allows it to be manipulated

SPST – single pole single throw

stability – the resistance to change in a system

stain resistant – fabric that is chemically protected against stains affecting the fibres

star profile – a diagram to show a food's characteristics

static – a constant load

stencil cutter – a plotter which can cut card or thin plastic sheet

sterile – with no micro-organisms present

stiffness – the ability to resist bending

stock sizes – the standard sizes of material that suppliers have in stock

stroke – the movement of the piston in a pneumatic cylinder

structure – a body which resists forces without changing shape too much

struts – rigid members used in compression

sugars – used as sweeteners

summative evaluation – the final evaluation

switch – breaks an electrical circuit when a button, lever or toggle is operated

symbols – drawings which represent things

synthetic – a material that does not come from a natural source

system – a collection of linked things

T

tack – to join together with a removable stitch

tasting – eating or drinking to find out the texture or taste of food or drink

tease apart – to gently pull apart

technical notebook – written comments about technical aspects of your project

template – a pattern, used to draw around

tensile strength – the load which a material can withstand

tension force – a pulling force

testing – trying out things

thermistors – temperature dependant resistors

thermoplastic – plastics that soften when heated, harden when cooled, and then can be heated and softened again many times

thermosets – plastics that, after being heated and softened during manufacture, cannot be changed or softened by heating again

ties – flexible members used in tension

time constant – time taken to charge a capacitor

timer – a circuit which stays on or off for a time after receiving an input signal

timetable – a chart showing when you hope to complete parts of the project or topic

torque – the force of twisting

torsion – twisting

toxic – dangerous to health

transfer paper – colour designs can be transferred onto fabric by ironing

triangulation – triangles are the strongest elements of a structure and cannot be deformed

TTL – transistor transistor logic

U

ultrasonics – vibrating things together until they heat up and melt

V

valve – controls the distribution of air in a system

vegan – someone who does not eat any animal products

vegetarian – someone who does not eat meat

velocity ratio – a comparison of the distances moved by the effort and the load

veneer – a very thin sheet of wood shaved from large piece of wood

vitamins – found in vegetables and fruit, keep you healthy

WXYZ

warp – twist or distort

wastage – shaping by removing materials

work hardening – when hammered or bent, metals get harder to work

working voltage – the maximum voltage that can be applied to a capacitor

woven – threads joined together to make fabrics

Index